The Silent SUICIDE

THE LINK BETWEEN PTSD, ADDICTION AND BREAST CANCER

by

MARGOT DRAGON MAOM L.AC. HYPNOTIST

The Silent Suicide

All information, techniques, ideas and concepts contained within this publication are of the nature of general comment only and are not in any way recommended as individual advice. The intent is to offer a variety of information to provide a wider range of choices now and in the future, recognizing that we all have widely diverse circumstances and viewpoints. Should any reader choose to make use of the information contained herein, this is their decision, and the contributors (and their companies), authors and publishers do not assume any responsibilities whatsoever under any condition or circumstances. It is recommended that the reader obtain their own independent advice.

First Edition 2021

Dedication

There is no right or wrong way to live your life.

The experience is yours, and yours alone. I am thankful for the people who have come into my life. They have shown me the dark crevices of myself that I ignored for so many years. Without experiencing the emotions that I allowed myself to feel, I would never have taken this difficult journey. And to them, I say much love, and may your life's journey take you to all the places you need to go.

Preface

Every kid gets stuck on something, and my something was "why?" I was relentless. Constantly seeking to understand "why?" It's the *soul* reason I wrote this book. My quest was to make sense of the complications of life and to figure out the patterns of trauma so that I could understand the "why?" No one deserves to be sick, let alone get cancer or die from it, and people deserve to have some form of understanding of how diseases develop. I hope that this book piques your curiosity, and I hope it makes you question everything, and this book gives you the opportunity to explore a new perspective towards the formation of illnesses. The Universe and God are always on your side. Have faith that something has guided you to this book for a good reason. The lessons are yours and yours alone, and what you will find here is what you're ready to discover.

One love.

Table of Contents

CHAPTER 1

Introduction

Don't Shoot the Messenger

This book is simply a mere observation of what I have seen in my life, both personally and professionally, and is only a theory based on my experience. This book will probably trigger many people for different reasons, which can be good if you want to explore where that emotional reaction came from. I am only a seed planter or guide. It's up to the individual reader to find and discover their own truths. This book is not out to discredit anyone or anything. It's just my exploration of my journey to a deeper understanding. I hope it allows you to go deep into the ugly parts of yourself that you've hidden away and never claimed before. Since finding oneself is a personal journey of discovery, we can remove the veil of hiding that we have used far too long.

Life, if we allow it, can be a sobering and rewarding experience. But we cannot fool ourselves out of our pain and trauma. The Universe, or God, is an empowering life force, and will give us the reflections that we need to see to heal ourselves. If you choose to avoid the messages, then your diseases and emotional issues will worsen. When we finally accept that life is how it should be, and not the fantasy or lie we have been telling ourselves it is as part of our coping, then we can truly begin to live and to heal our authentic selves.

I have noticed during the Coronavirus that many people have modified their patterns of behavior. This much-needed transition will help us realign ourselves with the laws of the Universe and the planet.

This book is not a substitute for any medical or psychological advice, so please consult with your physician if you have any of those issues.

"We cannot solve our problems with the same thinking we used to create them."
Albert Einstein--Physicist

"Nothing records the effects of a sad life so graphically as the human body."
Naguib Mahfouz, Palace of Desire

My Journey

There is an epidemic that's running rampant across the globe; it's called suicide and happens daily among our families, friends, or strangers. No one can truly understand the depths of the pain and trauma one who commits suicide has endured.

My father was a Captain in the Army during WWII. My parents were social drinkers, with daily 5 o'clock cocktails. I was the youngest of four siblings; When my mother was pregnant with me, my parents decided that my oldest brother David, who was 14 and a high-functioning autistic, should be placed in a state mental institute. In the 1960s doctors would recommend to parents of an autistic or mentally handicapped child to relinquish their parental rights to their own children. I could only imagine the hurt and devastation my parents must have felt -- especially my mother, who was eight months pregnant with me at that time. I believe that this decision killed my parents. My mother struggled with manic depression after this and spent time in a mental institution. My father suffered from severe depression and became an abusive alcoholic who killed himself when I was 6.

I have thought to myself, what impact this had on my own life, since I was so young. Could it have affected me, since I barely knew my father? I realized that it caused subtle consequences in my life, from being fearful of men, to crying at movies when I see the interaction of a father with his daughter. I still feel the loss of meaningful teachings between father and daughter, since I never really experienced them.

Instead, I had wonderful neighbors who took me in as their extra daughter. I like to call myself daughter number 4 ½, but my second dad calls me "number 6." They are a kind and *loving* family, a husband and wife with five wonderful daughters who showed me the *love,* acceptance, and compassion that my hurting parents were unable to give.

The impact of our childhood carries through our adult years. But unfortunately, we ignore these scars, unbeknownst to us, only to create significant problems in the future. Our "wall," the moment we must either change or face the consequences, is what determines our will to survive, and the quality of our lives.

Talking about suicide is never an easy thing, and unfortunately, I know firsthand what it's like to lose someone close to you. When my father committed suicide, it left me with many unanswered questions. As humans, we tend to strive to put overwhelming events

in a logical order so that we can cope. Some view suicide as a selfish act: "How could they leave me?

What am I supposed to do now? How will I ever make ends meet?"

We become overwhelmed with our emotions: grief and sadness, anger, pensiveness, fear, and a loss of joy.

But what if the suicide rate was much higher, and right under our noses? What if there was another kind of suicide, *The Silent Suicide?*

As humans, we have an innate connection to nature's five elements earth, fire, water, wood, and wind and the laws of physics. Newton's Third Law states: "For every action, there is an equal and opposite reaction," and that pertains to everything in our lives. Thus, the body's physiology is bound together mysteriously by chemical, vibrational, emotional, and physical reactions.

What if The Silent Suicide is called cancer?

What if someone is hurting so badly from either a spoken or unspoken trauma that it kills them? How many times have we watched numerous people get cancer, and we say "They've done nothing wrong in their lives to deserve this horrible disease." But, what if some part of them, deep down secretly, wanted to die as a way to end their suffering from those unresolved traumas from childhood, and they just wanted to "check out."

This book will look at the connection to PTSD, the hurt inner child, and *The Silent Suicide* called cancer.

Like many others, I have watched some wonderful people die from cancer, and not only is the disease horrible, but in some cases, the cancer treatment is horrible.

The purpose of this book is to encourage people to think at a deeper level, which may help them heal from their cancers. This book is from my experience and observation alone and is not a substitute for medical advice. The reality is, you will find what you choose to seek, and nothing more. Since "coming clean with yourself" can be a gut-wrenching process that empowers the mind, body, and spirit, when something happens in your life, learn to seek the hidden meaning or lesson. There are no accidents, just a series of divine events that can lead you down a path of healing, if you choose to do so. Unfortunately, what you decide to stuff away inside will reappear as disease and the suffering of your hurt inner child.

CHAPTER 2

Traditional Chinese Medicine (TCM)

Traditional Chinese Medicine has been around for over 4,000 years, virtually unchanged. It follows the laws of nature, and no matter how you want to change them, your body will follow those laws.

I chose to work in Traditional Chinese Medicine because Western Medicine didn't make sense, or sit well, with my *soul*. It seemed to me to defy the laws of nature. "It's not nice to fool Mother Nature," as the saying goes. She is big, powerful, and she'll always win. I am also fascinated with the Laws of Physics, especially Newton's Third Law: "For every action, there is an equal and opposite reaction." Like it or not, we are connected to these laws. We may spend a lifetime fooling ourselves or trying to bend or defy these laws, but eventually, reality (like a rubber band) will snap back at us. Think about how many times we've yelled at kids, spouses, parents, or friends, saying, "If you do that, you're going to get hurt." Yet, we fail to see the silent wounds that start to erode our consciousness and our bodies over time, like droplets of water, until disease happens.

Traditional Chinese Medicine (TCM) view of the elements, organs, tastes, and emotions:

In TCM, all the organs and tissues are interconnected to the five elements of nature: earth, fire, water, wood, and metal.

These five elements are connected to five emotions: pensiveness/thoughtlessness, joy/love, fear, anger/frustration/worry, and grief/sadness.

According to Traditional Chinese Medicine, all diseases start as unresolved emotions.

In Traditional Chinese Medicine the organs use the same name as western medicine, but the diagnosis is different. San jiao is a special organ in TCM that works similarly to the lymphatic system. At times if you are diagnosed according to TCM there may be nothing wrong with the organ if you went to your western medical doctor. And sometimes the two medicines overlap but the diagnosis terms will be different.

Organs, Emotions, and Elements:

Liver: What if you're an alcoholic? Alcohol is metabolized in the liver, which is connected to the emotions of anger/frustration. Have you ever heard the saying, "an angry drunk," or what about "being so angry I can't see straight?" The liver is also responsible for the eyes and eyesight. The liver is connected to the gall bladder, which is connected to the emotion of worry. These organs are part of the wood element.

Heart: What if you are broken-hearted? The heart is related to joy or love. "Be still, my beating heart." Or "he makes my heart race." "She died of a broken heart." "*My Heart is on Fire.*" (Song by Asta, songwriters Binnie Ireland Asta Evelyn, Young Cal, 2014). The heart is also connected to the small intestine, san jiao, pericardium, and the element fire.

Lungs: What if you are overcome with grief and sadness? The lungs are related. "Crying your lungs out." "Screaming your lungs out." When a child cries, we say they have a "healthy set of lungs." The lung and large intestine are connected to the metal element.

Kidney: Have you ever been so scared, you wet yourself? How about when you were a kid, and afraid of monsters, and you would pee in your sleep? The kidney and the urinary bladder are related to the emotion of fear. These are connected to the water element.

Spleen: Have you ever not wanted to think about something? Ever done something without thinking? Ever been called "thoughtless?" The spleen, stomach, and pancreas are related to the emotion pensiveness, or deep thought and are connected to the earth element.

Many have experienced this modern plague called "cancer," but few realize that the root cause of this is *The Silent Suicide*. In Traditional Chinese Medicine, the five elements in nature are associated with 14 organs, body tissues, and five emotions: pensiveness, grief/sadness, anger/frustration/worry, joy, and fear. As our subconscious struggles with these unresolved emotions we stuffed down, we learn to use coping skills such as addictions, unhealthy relationships with ourselves and others, and unhealthy diets.

Over the years, the unhealthy food choices we've made helped us stuff our unresolved emotions, and in turn, have weakened our body's immune system. As our immune system weakens, our healthy cells can no longer maintain their balance; they start to mutate and grow cancer. This process of stuffing the unresolved emotions with poor eating choices can contribute to cancer formation and is what I call *The Silent Suicide*.

There is a nourishing cycle in Traditional Chinese Medicine called the Mother-Child cycle, or the generation cycle. Think about how a mother nourishes her child, such as with touch, tone, nourishment, or breast-feeding. When this cycle experiences a disconnect, both mother and child will seek alternatives for breast milk, or nourishment for the relationship -- any option to help regenerate the relationship or bond. These options may include unhealthy food choices, bad relationships, addictions, or other destructive behaviors. **Many will seek out dairy products, which can be a harmful supplement to replace breast milk. It provides two main ingredients, the sedative tryptophan, and the sugar lactose, which acts similarly to cocaine in the brain. Hence, it re-addicts the person who feels deprived of the nourishment of the relationship. When someone continually uses products that contain dairy, the body's autoimmune system starts to struggle. As a result, it starts to create illnesses that are related to unresolved psychological traumas.**

Meridians in Traditional Chinese Medicine (TCM)

Several meridians run through the chest area; each one has a special connection to breast cancer.

The Kidney Meridian/kidney organ: according to TCM, is the organ that receives the essence from our parents. It's also interconnected with the teeth, brain, bones, and head hair. Each organ is connected to an emotion, and the kidney is connected to the emotion of fear (flight or freezing in PTSD). The point on the meridian located on the chest is called Shen Feng, meaning "God's heart, or territory of the heart or Gods." It's essential to understand the connection to breast cancer and the link to this meridian, because of metastasis to the brain or bone, which is directly related to the kidney in Traditional Chinese Medicine. Cancer involving these organs is related to an unresolved fear (flight or freezing in PTSD). In addition, the kidney is connected to fertility, sex or sexuality, and is the essence from our parents. Emotionally, it's related to an unresolved fear from the mother/child relationship. The meridian is located on either side of the breastbone or sternum. The Kidney Meridian also interconnects its paired organ the urinary bladder, and the liver (anger/frustration), Heart and Pericardium Meridians (joy/love), and the Spleen Meridian (pensiveness, thoughtlessness)

Symptoms associated with the Kidney Meridian:

- Pain in the spine column
- Weakness in the legs or knees
- Heat sensations in the bottom of the feet
- Pain in the inner thighs

Symptoms of the kidney TCM organ: infertility, menstrual issues, bedwetting, asthma, dry mouth, swelling, frequent urination, prostate issues.

The Liver Meridian/liver organ also runs through the chest, and interconnects with its paired organ the gall bladder (worry). One of the points located on the chest is called Chi Men, "to hope, or the gate to hope." This meridian runs right below the nipple and maybe be closely related to ductal cancers. The emotion related to the liver is anger/ frustration (fight, in PTSD), and many breast cancer cases metastasize to the liver. These can indicate the unresolved emotion of anger/frustration about the mother/child bond. I have found there are a lot of women who have their gall bladders removed due to excessive worry from a TCM point of view. **Commonly, unresolved fear in children becomes anger or frustration in adults.**

Symptoms associated with the Liver Meridian: side or flank pain, a sensation of fullness in the rib cage and chest, pain in the lower abdomen.

Symptoms of the liver TCM organ: burping, acid reflux, migraines on the side of the head or eyes, vision issues, muscle spasms, sighing, hiccups.

The Spleen Meridian/spleen organ: travels to its paired organ the stomach, and to the sides of the breast. The point closest to the nipple is called the "Celestial Gully Stream," which connects the outer and center parts of the breast. The spleen is related to the emotions of pensiveness, deep thought, or thoughtlessness. The Spleen Meridian connects to the meridians of the Lung (grief and sadness), Gall Bladder (worry) and the Liver (anger/frustration). This meridian also connects to the organs: stomach (pensiveness, deep thought, thoughtlessness), heart (joy/love), lung (grief/sadness).

Symptoms associated with the Spleen Meridian: lack of hunger due to a full sensation, feeling slow and heavy, tired, sluggish, slow digestion, swelling, or heaviness in the inner thigh or knee area.

Symptoms associated with the Spleen organ: loose stools, fatigue, jaundice, gas or bloating, abdominal distention, vomiting.

The Ren Meridian, which runs straight down the center of your body from your head to your crotch. The main point of the chest is called the "Middle Chest," which links to the organs: small intestine and san jiao (heart: joy/love), spleen (pensiveness/deep thought, or thoughtlessness), and liver (anger/frustration).

Symptoms related to the Ren Meridian: Depression and anxiety felt in the chest, or heart palpitations.

Understanding the Meridians helps explain why these unresolved emotions can contribute to the risk of forming cancers. Unfortunately, I have met many people both personally and professionally who have suffered from these unresolved emotions and who develop cancer over the years.

The breast is the nourishment between mother and child, and when there's a trauma or a disconnection between mother and child, a disease such as breast cancer can form. In an article dated February 13, 2019, in *People* magazine, *Kate Middleton Admits She Was Very Naive as a Parent*, by Simon Perry and Stephanie Petit, the Duchess of Cambridge stated: "Over the last 8 years, working with charities, I've met some of our leading experts in mental health, addiction, family breakdown, homelessness, and education. They have taught me over and over again that the root cause of so many of today's social problems can be traced right back to the very earliest years of a person's life, often over generations."

Remember Newton's Third Law: "For every action, there is an equal and opposite reaction." In Traditional Chinese Medicine, social or emotional problems are equal to physical ailments. Mind, body, and spirit are interconnected, and each organ and body tissue are attached to an emotion.

There is one more meridian associated with breast cancer that we must consider, especially when it comes to metastasis.

The San Jiao Meridian: is related to the heart organ in TCM and emotions, joy, or love, and has a similar function to the lymphatic system. It is responsible for the

movement of waste, foods, and fluids throughout the body and covers the same area of the body as the Chakras in Indian culture.

There are three parts of the San Jiao:

Upper Jiao: head and chest, breast, heart, and lungs.

Middle Jiao: stomach, liver, spleen, and gall bladder.

Lower Jiao: kidneys, intestines, reproductive organs, and urinary bladder.

The lymph glands in the armpit are common area for breast cancer to spread to. Located here is the acupuncture point called the "Supreme Spring" on the Heart Meridian, which is connected to other internal organs such as the lungs, pericardium, large intestine, small intestine, and the san jiao. The San Jiao Meridian crosses the diaphragm into the abdomen, liver, spleen, stomach, and pancreas, which is another area of metastasis. The San Jiao Meridian also extends from the chest into the neck and head, another possible route for cancer to spread to the head. The last and final leg of the San Jiao meridian flows down into the lower part of the body, where the kidneys, urinary bladder, and all the reproductive organs reside. As the San Jiao works at eliminating cancerous cells, it could, in the process, unwittingly expose other organs to the disease.

Because there will always be many interconnected systems involved with a disease in TCM, all possibilities should be looked at and taken into consideration.

CHAPTER 3

Traditional Chinese Medicine - 5 Elements and Emotions:

Wood Element: Spring, East, Liver and Gall Bladder, Anger or Frustration, and Worry, Sour:

In Traditional Chinese Medicine, the liver is responsible for the emotions of anger, frustration as well as moving energy throughout the body that is known as the Qi or life force. The liver is responsible for construction or destruction, both internally or externally, or the action/reaction or fight in PTSD. For example, if a child must "choose" loving one parent/guardian over another or the child must ignore their own needs and wants or their individualism is suppressed by a parent, the child can become reactive or destructive (fight, anger, frustration). Parents might exhibit the totalitarian "my way or the highway" type of parenting, which puts a great deal of stress on a child, affecting the child's ability to be flexible by stagnating the liver's energy. As a result, the child can become inflexible or stubborn, pitch fits, or pout and feel they must abandon their own needs. As these children get older, they may become rebellious, spiteful, self-punishing or self-rejecting -- or afraid of humiliation. The child can become emotionally or physically stuck at the age when the trauma occurred, and as a result they may be filled with self-anger and may constantly repeat the original trauma throughout their lives. They might have an aggressive drive towards business, relationships, sports, or other enterprises. However, they can also withdraw or retreat. The stagnation of wood energy leads to the formation of diseases, stabbing pain, acid reflux, migraines, burping and tumors. Even though it remains rooted, their liver or wood energy is constantly moving and adapting to its ever-changing environment. They must stay flexible to adapt to change quickly in order to flourish.

Water Element: Winter, North, Kidney and Urinary Bladder, Fear, Salty:

Have you ever been so scared you peed in your pants, or wet the bed when you were a child? Maybe you fear loud noises? The kidney is responsible for our brain, blood, bones, and hearing, according to Traditional Chinese Medicine. The kidney essence is our life force, fertility, sexuality, and what we inherited from our parents. As kids, many things scare us. As we look back, it may seem silly or childish, but when you're a kid, these things had a significant impact. Fear gives us healthy boundaries and keeps us safe. But when we are faced with situations that make us fearful as children, especially if they are repeated, fear no longer keeps us secure; instead, fear becomes our paralyzing "best friend."

The kidney or water element is related to the fright and freezing in PTSD. The water element, our life force, is also tied to death. The death of a parent, sibling, or loved one can often cause our fears to become irrational -- understandably. "I won't love you cause you'll die, or I won't do this because it may kill me." Children like this who have separation anxiety can also experience fear of illness or hospitalization.

Those with an out-of-balance water element may have infertility issues, hearing difficulties, bone or arthritis issues, sexual issues, bladder or prostate issues, dental or brain issues.

When the water element is balanced, there will be a free flow of deep thought and consciousness, allowing people to look for the deeper meaning to life and the Universe. As a result, people will become more aware of their connections to God or the Universe and understand their relationship to a higher purpose.

Metal Element: Autumn, West, Lung and Large Intestine, Grief and Sadness, Pungent:

The metal element is about taking in and releasing. People with predominant metal element will have the ability to seek out relevant others or information. When related tasks or relationships are completed, they will be able to let go. This phase represents our maturing by letting go of our role as a child to that of an adult.

This phase is about mutual relationships, letting go, and processing our grief and sadness. It's essential to allow ourselves to breathe, both emotionally and physically, in order to let go of our unresolved feelings. When a person has a healthy metal element, he or she will be responsible for his or her actions, thoughts, and emotions.

When the metal element is out of balance, the person will have difficulties with a long-term relationship, or deep, meaningful connections, or may feel disconnected from God or the Universe. Some people will struggle with their own sexual identity to fit in with someone else's lifestyle, experience self-esteem issues, or lose themselves in a relationship. *Love* will seem more of a possession than a mutual relationship.

Earth Element: Indian Summer, Center, Spleen, Stomach and Pancreas, Pensiveness:

The earth element is all about digestion, nourishment both physically and emotionally, and any oral fixation. Digestion is your emotional and physical self-nourishment. It's related to bonds and boundaries and is also about separation and one's ability to distinguish self from others.

There are many times I ask my patients what kinds of food they eat, and who fed them as a child. When I treat the patient, this helps me understand where specific eating patterns might have contributed to, or worsened, their illness. If the person feeding you experienced trauma, they'll have difficulties nourishing themselves. How will they ever teach you self-nourishment, emotionally or physically? Trauma, shock, or PTSD "freezes" a person, both emotionally and physically, often at the age their trauma occurred. How many times have we told an adult that he or she is acting like a baby or a child? They may be so traumatized, that's their natural behavior. Their diet will be basic and childlike: frozen food, microwavable food, fast foods, soda, candy, and snacks. They may say things like, "I just grab some food," like children 2-4 years old do. People with a healthy earth element will be calm and grounded or "rock-solid," and have a centered presence. These people know their self-worth and have safe boundaries. Without this balance, someone will seem superficial, blow things off, and say, "everything is fine," even when their world is crumbling around them. They might seem "over the top," and many will say they had a *loving* relationship with their mothers, only to find out that their emotional needs as children were unsupported, or that there were no safe boundaries.

The earth element is also related to breast-feeding, since it is the first oral fixation or addiction. Since this phase is all about the mother-child bond, safe and healthy boundaries are vitally important. Many will have an absentee father, with a mother who becomes overly protective because of their unresolved traumas. As a result, they become dependent on others to take care of them. Or they might be clingy types and feel uncomfortable facing situations by themselves. This lack of self-sufficiency leads to even more significant problems in life. These are "the world revolves around me" type of people who may seem immature or childish, wanting their "mommy." Their diet will replace their original oral fixation of suckling and wanting only comfort foods. They may also appear to be victims, have a "woe is me" attitude, or become a constant worrier.

Fire Element: Summer, South, Heart and Pericardium, Small Intestine, San Jiao, Joy or Love:

The fire element is related to someone's creativity, passion, and the emotions of love or joy. When a child starts saying yes to things, this developmental stage is when he or she begins to bond with the parent of sexual preference. A spouse can become envious of that relationship. Many parents suppress creative children because they might believe it's not "practical" for the future. How will you make money? Our creativity helps us see the world through fresh, childlike eyes, which brings us happiness and joy. Suppression of their feelings and creativity can cause a child to become compliant for fear of losing or alienating his or her parent or caregiver. The spontaneity of the explorer allows the child to grow naturally and independently.

The fire element is the most significant one that motivates people to create beautiful works of art, science, poetry, inventions, and creations with passionate motivation. When these children are withheld from their creative outlets, it may lead to living a "double life" or to please others solely to gain or keep their *love,* while their authentic selves remain closeted.

A parent or guardian who does not love themselves will be unable to teach a child what is joyful or see what is joyful within a child. Likewise, when we fail to nourish ourselves, we can neither give nor receive *love* from others.

CHAPTER 4

Traditional Chinese Medicine -- Five Musical Tones

Have you ever wondered why kids can listen to the same song over and over and over....... again? Well, it's because they are healing their body with the music.

The Pentatonic Scale in music is over 50,000 years old. The major keys are associated with upbeat and happy songs, while the minor keys are for sadder songs. Music, a fantastic tool to help you heal and reprogram many parts of your brain, is used to help Alzheimer's and Parkinson's patients as well. By activating the parts of the brain responsible for our feel-good drug, dopamine, music regulates our body overall regarding mood, emotions, blood pressure, sleep, etc....

As children, one of the first songs we hear is "Brahms Lullaby," by Johannes Brahms, which is in the key of E. In Traditional Chinese Medicine, this tone calms the liver and gall bladder, making the anger, frustration, or worry melt away for both baby and parents. Other songs, such as "Hush, Little Baby," by unknown author, and "Rock-A-Bye, Baby," by unknown author are in the key of G, which is related to the heart and the emotions love and joy; "Twinkle, Twinkle, Little Star," a poem by Jane Taylor, 1806 is in the key of C, which is connected to the spleen and the emotions of pensiveness/deep thought or thoughtlessness.

Have you ever tried listening to music that you hate, then changing the channel to classical music? Notice how your body changes, so that you feel calmer and more relaxed. Why is soothing music played at yoga class or spas? Because it's a winning combination, just like when you sing or listen to music to help reset your mood or soothe your mind. Your brain is doing a happy dance, so practice changing your moods by playing or listening to music. I recently watched the film, *Take Me Home: The John Denver Story,* about the musician. I noticed that anytime he felt emotional, he wrote a song about it, often in the keys of D (grief and sadness) and A(fear).

Another great songwriter, Gordon Lightfoot, wrote a song called "Carefree Highway" about an experience with a woman who *loved* him and then left him. The original song was in the key of E, which is associated with liver and gall bladder, and the emotions anger, frustration or worry. (TCM)

The other classic of Gordon's is "If You Could Read My Mind," which is about the breakup of his first marriage. It's written in the key of G, which is related to heart and the emotions love or joy or, in this case, the lack of joy/love. His song "The Wreck of the Edmond Fitzgerald" is written in the key of C, in which some people are uncomfortable talking about death or loss and is related to the spleen and the emotions pensiveness or deep thought or, in this case, not wanting to think about loss.

One of the most famous songwriters of all time is Dolly Parton, who has written thousands of songs. One of her most popular songs is "I Will Always Love You," which she wrote when she was trying to leave the Porter Wagoner Show. The song was written in the key of D, which is related to the lung and large Intestine in TCM and the emotions grief and sadness. Porter decided he didn't want Dolly to leave the show, but Dolly knew she had to move on with her career.

In Traditional Chinese Medicine, the five elements discussed earlier also pertain to five musical notes or tones. They are also associated with the five voices used in diagnosing a patient: crying, wording, calling, roaring, and singing. Most of you are familiar with the tones as the typical scale of C Major: Do, Re, Mi, Fa, So, La, Ti, Do .... You all know the song from *Sound of Music* that Julie Andrews sang... "Do-Re-Mi"

Wood: Liver and gall bladder are related to the emotion anger, the musical note E, and the tone Mi. This is someone who likes to give orders, or who scolds or shouts. Their voice will seem like they are calling. The more out of balance their liver and gall bladder are, the more the person scolds and shouts.

Earth: Spleen, stomach, and pancreas and the emotion pensiveness are connected to the musical note C, and the tone Do. These people have a singing quality to their voice, and they'll either sing a lot or not at all, depending on the health of their digestive system.

Metal: Lung and large intestine and the emotions grief and sadness are connected to the musical note D and the tone Re. These people will either cry too much or not at all, depending on their organs' health. There will be a crying quality to their voice if the lung and large intestine are out of balance.

Water: Kidney and urinary bladder, and the emotion fear, are connected to the musical note A and the tone La. They will have a roaring quality to their voice, or else they will groan when the kidney and bladder are out of balance.

Fire: Heart, small intestine, san jiao, and pericardium are connected to the emotion love, joy or lack of joy or love, and the musical note G or the tone So. These people will make mistakes with their wording while speaking, or they will laugh inappropriately.

Music helps align the body, mind, and spirit by activating many parts of the nervous system and the brain, so sing, dance, do yoga, or chant often. Do these activities every day to increase your vibrational frequency. As you do, you also increase your ability to heal, and to see a better picture of your connection to God or the Universe.

"Music can save your mortal soul."
- "Miss American Pie,"
- by Don McLean-Musician

"Music has healing power. It has the ability to take people out of themselves for a few hours."
- Elton John - Musician

"Music can heal the wounds that medicine cannot touch."
- Debasish Mridha - M.D.

CHAPTER 5

Chakras

There are seven main chakras in which our energy travels through our bodies and balances our mind, body, and spirit, which overlap with Traditional Chinese Medicine. Also, there are two main meridians in Traditional Chinese Medicine on which these chakras are found: the Governing Vessel or Du and the Conception Vessel or Ren. These meridians make a loop that your body's energy travels. The energy loop travels through the head, down the center of the face, to the chest, abdomen, and genitals. Then it travels up through the spine and back and up over the top of the head. Imagine an energetic Hula Hoop that you are straddling, from the top of your head to your crotch. This energetic loop passes through all the organs as well. When this energy flow is blocked, it will cause both emotional and physical symptoms. This will help us further understand the connection to breast cancer and its metastasis.

Crown Chakra - Sahasrara, Thousand Petal Lotus:

This area is located at the top of the head, equal to an acupuncture point called Du 20 or "100 Meetings." This chakra area brings awareness of our more significant connection to God, the Universe, and faith. The chakra is connected to our brain and nervous system, and to our enlightened spiritual connection or faith. It gives us the ability to know that all things are connected. The lotus flower seed develops in the darkness, in the mud below the water -- just as a baby forms in the womb. As we both -- the lotus and the baby -- grow and develop, we must navigate the muddy waters of our lives, ever reaching and growing towards the light.

It's only through hard work and self-determination that we find a greater understanding of our lives and our role within the Universe (the bigger cosmic picture). Then we can truly heal, with forgiveness and compassion towards ourselves and others. This Universal light, God, faith, enlightenment is what all creatures can achieve, and it's only by our constant deflection away from the light that we self-obstruct our view. We blind ourselves to our connection to God or the Universe that's constantly around us, which guides us through the mud within our lives. Those who remain stubborn and skeptical will continue to struggle in the mud, unable to see or have faith that the light is always there. When we close off to the truth, that produces muddy and clouded thoughts, which can contribute to brain cancers and other diseases of the brain. The brain in Traditional Chinese Medicine is related to the kidney, essence of life, connection to our parents, and emotion of fear. This is related to what we have inherited from our parents.

> **"Be gentle on yourself. You are a child of the universe, no less than the trees and the stars. In the noisy confusion of life, keep peace in your soul."**
> **Max Ehrmann - Writer**

Third-Eye Chakra, Anja, Beyond Wisdom:

This chakra is located between the eyebrows. In Traditional Chinese Medicine, this is the acupuncture point location called Yin Tang, or "Hall of Impression," the chakra of intuition and imagination. When this point is out of balance, it can lead to headaches, hearing issues, vertigo, allergies, or a heavy or watery sensation in the head. In TCM we like to call this the "Chill Out" point. It can affect your ability to concentrate or listen, and can cause you to be narrow-minded. This is where our intuition, self-reflection, and higher connection originate.

It's our first communication center in the womb, where we can feel our mother's emotions, as well as sense her thoughts. When she is under stress, we'll also react, and this is our first form of communication to the outside world. The Third Eye, the source of gut feeling or intuition, helps guide us through the muddy waters of life. Many of us ignore these thoughts Although all day long, we receive these notifications. It might be a number on a license plate, usually an angel number, or a random phone call or meeting in which someone is relaying a message. We each have a gang of superheroes -- archangels, angels, spirit guides, and transitioned friends and relatives who are guiding us and cheering us on every day. You can't hide or outrun them, because they're always there, only needing one thing from you: **Permission to help.**

There are no random accidents, just a series of divine events to guide us to our greater self and higher good.

Yes, you can spend all your time down in the dumps, as a victim. But there is just as much good as there is bad, and it's all around you. If you only focus on negative possibilities, that is what you will surround yourself with. On the other hand, you can decide it was an absolute blessing, a healing lesson to enable you to grow closer to your real authentic self.

**Victory or victim, it's your choice.
Remember free will?**

**"It isn't the mountains ahead to climb that wear you out; it's the pebble in your shoe."
Muhammad Ali - Boxer**

Throat Chakra, Vishudda, Complete Purity:

This chakra is in the throat or cervical spine area. On the front of the neck is the acupuncture point called Ren 22, or "Heaven Projection." On the spine is the acupuncture point Du 14 or "Big Vertebrae." This chakra is related to teeth, gums, mouth issues, TMJ, thyroid, neck issues and hearing problems. This is the area of communication, peace, truth, your ability to listen, lying, speaking issues such as Tourette's Syndrome, stuttering, hearing problems, seeing life from different directions, or withdrawal. This area includes the shoulders, representing your ability to shoulder your responsibilities. The burdens in life, or the "weight of the world upon your shoulders."

Have you ever watched someone before they get hit? Their shoulders rise up to protect their vulnerable neck. It's related to our ability to speak the truth and to active listening with an open heart. Many women suffer from thyroid problems; those with an under-active thyroid are withholding what needs to be said. Those with an overactive thyroid are talking too much about things that are truly not important, lying or redirecting the conversation. Our neck and shoulders stiffen up if we fail to look at life from different directions. How many of us are afraid to say something because we fear rejection from someone, when all the while we're rejecting ourselves? —Too many of us.

Expressing yourself freely is an awesome superpower, and saying what needs to be said is one of the most liberating things you can do. Maybe this is why so many people drink or do drugs -- so they can speak freely, perhaps for the first time in their lives. What about all the deathbed confessions? Are we truly going to wait that long to say what we think? Until our inner child feels safe enough to speak out, and so we silently think, "What are you going to do to me? I'm dying, so you can't touch me." Maybe we should spend more time confessing, so we can start living rather than merely existing. If you fail to have the courage to speak, then write, sing, or create, so you can get them out without self-shame, guilt, or other negative repressed thoughts. Parents often shame and suppress their kids, rather than letting them express themselves.

Allow your self-empowerment to flourish every day.

"The intimacy that arises in listening and speaking the truth is only possible if we can open to the vulnerability of our own hearts. Breathing in, contacting the life that is right here, is our first step. Once we have held ourselves with kindness, we can touch others in a vital and healing way."
Tara Brach - Psychologist

Heart Chakra, Anahata, Unbeaten:

Located in the area of the chest and heart (joy/love or lack of joy/love, Traditional Chinese Medicine) and lung (grief and sadness) and the breast (connection to mother and child). In Traditional Chinese Medicine, this area is equal to an acupuncture point called Ren 22 or "Chest Center." Some of the emotional issues associated with this chakra being out of balance include: Suppressed in love, codependency, shyness, loneliness, worthlessness, shame, and disappointment. These contribute to physical ailments such as asthma, breast cancer, breast lumps, lymphatic issues, and cardiac issues.

This chakra is the area of the unbeatable sound and beautiful vibration that radiates from our chest into the outer world and emits the frequency of love. We generate the unique emotion of love that no other person can give, and its only direction is outward. So many of us are dependent on whether someone *loves* us, but this is only a false hope based on the needs of our broken inner child. The reality is that we are on this life journey as a collection of individuals who each have a unique way of learning. This allows us to connect to our higher self, God, and the Universe. There's no right or wrong, and it's essential to accept someone else's path.

There may be times when someone comes into your life and helps guide you on your journey; some of those lessons can be intolerably cruel. However, when we take the time to reflect and see the bigger picture, we can understand the suffering we have endured. If you cannot see the love within yourself, and you seek it from another, you will most likely attract the same vibrational frequency of your unresolved trauma. So many of us are struggling to find that fleeting *love*. Just think about something you love or that brings you joy, and you will find it's not the person, animal, place, or thing-- but the thought you choose to generate about it.

"When I loved myself enough, I began leaving whatever wasn't healthy. This meant people, jobs, my own beliefs, and habits – anything that kept me small. My judgment called it disloyal. Now I see it as self-loving."
Kim Mc Millen - Author

Solar Plexus Chakra, Manipura, City of Jewels:

This chakra is equal to an acupuncture point in the stomach area called Ren 12 or "Middle Cavity," and is also related to the element fire. The area covers the navel to the solar plexus, and the organs pancreas, stomach, spleen (pensiveness/thoughtless), and liver and gall bladder (anger and worry) in Traditional Chinese Medicine. It's the source of metabolism, acid reflux, eating disorders, and indigestion. Some of the emotional issues associated with this chakra being out of balance would be: anger, fear, worry, hate or too much responsibility, guilt and shame, and fear of losing control. It's the chakra of self-responsibility and your power, your intestinal fortitude, gut instincts, willpower, and the ability to transform. It's where you make goals, plans, create desires, and set intentions and personal boundaries.

Many traumatized children have frequent tummy aches, emotional outbursts or fits of anger. **All physical symptoms are the result of emotions that are unable to be expressed.** Parents need to understand the deeper meaning of what is going on in a child. I know that many parents are overwhelmed and get caught up in the matter at hand, so it's essential to slow down and take the time to see the whole picture. In children, since sugar in various foods can be a coping mechanism for stress, they are using the sugar as a relaxant -- just as adults use alcohol.

> **"It's not the actions of others that trouble us, but rather our own judgments, remove these judgments, and resolve to let go of your anger, and it will already be gone."**
> **Marcus Aurelius - Roman emperor**

Navel Chakra, Svadhistana,
Dwelling Place of Self:

This chakra is related to the element water. Its area covers the sexual organs, uterine or bladder problems and prostate (these are all related to the kidney/urinary bladder in Traditional Chinese Medicine, and the emotion fear, and the element water). In TCM, this chakra is located on the belly button and at the location of an acupuncture point called the Ren 8 or "Spirit Gate." It is responsible for your feelings of self-worth, sexuality, creativity, female energy, and the formation of life, and is related to wellness, abundance, pleasure, and joy. When this chakra is out of balance, it can lead to fear of change, depression, addiction, emotional eating, sexual issues, jealousy, envy, and possessiveness. This chakra can be affected by molestation or sexual abuse, and whatever personal attributes have been taken without permission. When I see that a child's or adult's weight is mostly in the belly (pregnancy belly), that means they have unresolved issues with their mother, which could have occurred while their mother was pregnant with them.

How many children wet the bed or pee on themselves? Many of those children have these issues. Children are naturally curious and creative, and when their emotions and creativity get stifled or devalued, they lose their ability to freely self-express. There are various ways for children to express their creativity, such as writing, drawing, creating plays, fairy tales, music, painting, or crafts, which helps encourage children to take risks through healthy outlets.

> **"Creativity involves breaking out of established patterns in order to look at things in a different way."**
> **-- Edward de Bono - Physician**

Root Chakra, Muladhara, Root Support:

These are the roots of your life, which are related to the earth element. This involves your physical identity and your feeling of being grounded. When you are in balance, you will feel supported and have all your essential survival needs, making you feel safe. The root chakra is about your ability to trust or distrust, and your ability to let go. This area covers adrenals, kidneys, colon, rectum, spinal column, bones, prostate, and issues with legs and feet (all related to the kidney in TCM and to the emotion of fear). In Traditional Chinese Medicine, this chakra is at the base of the spine. It correlates with an acupuncture point called Du 3 or "Lumbar Yang Gate," which is for lower back pain, sciatica, urinary issues, leg issues, and infertility issues. The root chakra is also related to abandonment, self-criticism, abandonment of a *loved* one, and betrayal of trust. This chakra is also associated with something that threatens survival, such as rape or violence, or life-fearing events. When I see a patient who has the most weight around their hips, I always ask if they have been sexually abused, molested, or fondled.

People add weight in the area that has been traumatized as a form of protection.

Children get uprooted in their lives through moving, the addition of a sibling or a stepparent, divorce, and many other things that may cause them to be clingy to a parent, a blanket, or a stuffed animal -- or they may have bedwetting issues. Children who poop on themselves may have experienced sexual abuse or inappropriate touching, which is their subconscious way of protecting themselves.

> **"Two of the greatest gifts we can give our children are roots and wings."**
>
> **Hodding Carter - Author *Where Main Street Meets the River***

CHAPTER 6

Father, Son, and Holy Ghost--or Mind, Body, and Spirit:

Think of your body as three individual and dependent parts. Getting them to work together, however, is quite a story.

The Son (Inner Child), ~~or Body:~~

Our thinking can be rational, thoughtful, and adult-like, or it can be very child-like and reactionary, which the author John Bradshaw called "Inner Child." He stated that "Every one of us has a hurt inner child within us," and our families are as "sick as their secrets." Have you ever had the experience of going to the store, where some poor child has an absolute meltdown? It's the reflection of the inner child who didn't get *love,* time, attention, nourishing, nurturing, a pony, or whatever else we desired when we were young. It's that little person inside our bodies, who's mostly in our heads, with constant dialogue like, "NO! Am I pretty enough? You did that! Not me! That person's mean: I don't like them. Let's have candy or ice cream, and I'll feel better. Why don't they like me? I just want them to *love* me. I'll feel better when I go shopping."

Daily, this little controlling person tells us, as adults, what to do. No rational adult would ever take advice from a seven-year-old (inner child). Yet we do that subconsciously all the time! Our "inner child" has been through some horrible, unresolved experiences. They don't want to go through anything else that might cause them pain. So, to protect themselves, and us as rational adults, they tell us what to do, AND WE LISTEN! This is where our adult self gets into trouble. The stormy relationship, unhealthy foods, bad jobs, wrong place to live, you get it. Those decisions you made where you could kick yourself! Ah, yes, those decisions! This little crazy person whom no one in their right mind would listen to, and yet you (yes, you) are listening to them, closely. Rather than being your friend, they actually need your help. Ask yourself: "Would you want a seven-year-old driving your car? Or going to the grocery store and shopping for you? Would you want a seven-year-old to pay your bills?"

The list goes on, but I hope that you would say, "No, that's crazy." It's only you, the rational adult, who can help that crazy kid inside you to heal. So many of us stuffed down unresolved emotional traumas. It's our way of holding our hurt inner-child self, and yet not healing. We suppress our healing with food, alcohol, destructive relationships, bad jobs, drug abuse, and addictions. You name it, we use it. But here's the cool thing about God or the Universe: if you choose not to heal, that's okay, because the messages are only going to get much BIGGER. That's right, that whole conversation, "What? I can't hear you!" doesn't work when we're talking about God or the Universe, which is always doing its best to bring you back into balance with the laws of nature. These life situations, both good and bad, are your Divine messages to get your stuff together and heal! AMEN! Every relationship dump, every death, every car accident, every random person you meet has a message, and they are all of hope. Even in the worst situation, there will always be something about hope and healing. So when you reflect, choose wisely what you see. Every emotion, thought, or action you've ever had is a reflection of yourself: Mind, body, and spirit or Father, Son, and Holy Ghost. Learn to identify the "inner child" or adult self being reflected -- and WHY. The "inner child" is the one who imprints on the people around them, and as children, we do this to survive; when we try to fit in, we lose part of ourselves in the process.

Let's say that you *love* your dad, and every day when he comes home, he says, "I'd *love* a beer." So, being the loving child that you are, you run and get daddy a beer. Then one day, when you turn 18 and still underage to drink, your dad says to you, "Get me two beers." The loving child now imprints that *love* equals beer, because you *love* your dad; therefore, beer equals *love.* Imprinting is part of the survival process. In the future, you might have issues with alcohol, or find people who have problems with alcohol, so you can *love* and rescue them like you rescued daddy.

My seven-year-old self-had been holding me back for a long time. I thought because someone told me I was "dumb but intelligent" as a child, that I actually was. Besides, it came from a good source – my mom. I thought, how could I possibly get into med school? I was hopeless in math and chemistry, and I thought there was no way I could be a doctor, even though a friend of mine was going to pay for me to go to medical school. It was a FREE RIDE. All I had to do was go. But I didn't. So when I was busy holding myself back, the Universe, or God, said, "Oh, I got an idea!" and sent me a car accident. I was hit from behind, which eventually moved me forward in my life. I was holding myself back, it turns out, and that nasty PUSH FORWARD gave me the strength to leave home and go to med school.

The Father, or the Body:

Learning to say "no" is about holding a safe and loving space for you in your own life and making self-love your top priority. When we seek the illusion of *love* in others, we'll deny ourselves love, primarily when it's based on abandonment, shame, guilt, or fear. This, in turn, will increase the likelihood of enabling both of you to become alcoholics (example above). It will also increase the possibility of seeking *love* in the future. These behavior patterns have NOTHING to do with love and everything to do with the non-healing, dysfunctional pattern associated with alcoholism. Now you, the adult, (father or body) will calmly look at situations and assess them for what they are, whether it's an accident, death, or new *love*. There will always be a connection to your past, and your hurt inner child until you heal. When we allow ourselves to heal, we can release these situations quicker and quicker because we have already been down that road. The adult can always see the pattern and assess it for what it is. Sometimes this takes hours, or years, but if you truly want to heal and understand, there is no stopping you. As the father, body, or adult, you will be in tune with your emotions and with how your physical body is feeling. You will be able to make healthy adjustments in your life so you can live in peace and harmony within yourself. You will be able to rely on your intuition or gut feelings, and trust that you are being guided in your decision-making.

Holy Ghost, or Spirit:

This is your divine and enlightened self, the part of you that recognizes that you are connected to everyone and everything simultaneously. **You come from the source God or Universe, and you are of light and love.** It's the knowing, as you travel through life in your human form, that you are connected to a vast support group: spirit guides, angels, archangels, God, Buddha and of course, all your friends and family members, both alive and those who have transitioned out of their human selves. There's no greater power to know that you are not alone, and that a whole herd of entities have your back, no matter what situation you are facing. They are there to support you fully and completely, with the purest, most loving light you could ever imagine. To think of the possibility of even trying to be alone is what your seven-year-old hurt "inner child" is telling you, and it's the lie that you have believed probably for most of your life -- until you got a big message. So here is my tip. Connect NOW! You can ask for something goofy or crazy but ask for proof now. The sooner you realize this is true, the better and faster your healing and understanding will be.

My mom, whom I like to call Mamma, has transitioned, but she lets me KNOW she's around constantly. See, my mom's name is Georgia, so what do I see all the time? License plates from......Georgia. Some days she gets a little cockier and sends me a very clear message...When I was leaving my office, a big white truck was sitting in the parking lot directly in front. The plate was from Georgia and Clarke County. See, my Mamma's name is Georgia Clark. Sometimes when I'm worried about something, Mamma will send me a plate from Georgia that says, "In God We Trust." I say, "Okay, Mamma, trust God." Yup, she's around so much that my friends even point her out! Another friend whom I love dearly always makes sure I know she's around. She comes to me while I'm asleep, when I've had energy healing work done, as a doll who looks exactly like her or seeing her name, or a vehicle that reminds me of her. It happens so often; I find it very comforting and quite funny.

CHAPTER 7

When the Lights Go On

Emotions:

We as humans are fluid, and our emotions need to be fluid as well, for us to grow and heal. We cannot be bound to others, though, if we are to be fluid. That only brings in a false sense of security, as well as altering our behavior so we fit into someone else's life. Emotions need to come and go as they please. This will allow us to examine the source of the emotion, whether the adult self or our hurt inner child trying to overcome and resolve a previous trauma. We must be able to sit with our emotions as long as it takes, in order for them to resolve. Love is the same. Just as in all the emotions, it's based on a past experience, so the deeper the love, the deeper the trauma we must heal and overcome. Many of us find a way to stuff our emotions: Drugs, alcohol, sex, bad relationships, abuse, exercise, shopping, workaholism, food. Our soul is a clean slate that is unaffected by the plights of the human experience. Only our hurt "inner child" and body are affected.

When an emotion comes up, stop and take the time to think about "who" is having the emotion, and "what" past experience this reflects. When we take the time, we will discover that it's not about the situation, or even the person, but about what we feel and the expectations we have of others. I've had many patients say that they had wonderful relationships with their mothers, only to find out that their mothers were adopted, left in charge of other siblings, abandoned, mothers who had depression or addiction issues, or stayed with an abusive or alcoholic spouse. The inner child will always rationalize the *love* and the dysfunctional relationship, for fear of abandonment. The rational adult can reflect on the trauma, observe how it affected them, and see both the blessings and the trauma equally.

When we are babies, our body, mind, and spirit are more of one person, and the spirit knows what the mind and body need and want. As we grow up, we are exposed to outside influences, such as our parents, who tell us to eat what is on our plate, even though it may not be what our spirit is telling us we want to eat. The other influences that our parents (or whoever raised us) have are the patterns of unresolved traumas that they endured. As they stuff down their emotions, they teach us to do the same, and we grow up stuck in these unwanted patterns. Eventually, we all hit what I call the "wall" when we literally can go no further, are now forced to make a change or die. These "walls" are there to help correct what needs to be corrected. The more we don't face what is in front of us, the bigger the message.

I have experienced many "walls" in my life. One of the biggest involved my deepest *love* and my deepest trauma. I had such a deep *love* for another human being that I wanted to understand why I *loved* them so much. I felt completely at home, and that they were the air that I breathed. They were also very intuitive, and I would have visions while I slept of conversations between us. I wanted to understand the situation better, so I contacted an expert who recommended some books to read. I started looking at the situation as a massive science experiment. The reality was that I was a mother without a child, and they were a child without a mother, and we had complete transparency of each other's traumas. It was the most gut-wrenching grieving process I had ever experienced, but necessary for my healing. Forgiveness always comes across as unnecessary when you're not ready, but at this moment in my life, I was ready to receive, grieve and forgive. And I did. Not a day goes by that I don't *love* and appreciate this person who came into my life, and I hope someday they will feel the same, but this is my life's journey and my lessons of healing.

Idiot Lights:

I call the messages the idiot lights -- you know, like the ones in a car. Idiot lights can be both internal and external.

Internal idiot lights are any symptoms big or small that happen to your body. They warn you that something is not right; something needs to be fixed and addressed. Many people don't understand how to do maintenance on themselves. There's no manual to help us look up our problems. The body is the only vehicle that you travel through time and space in, so learn about how your body works as if your life depends on it --because it does. When we start to raise our own families, our kids will become triggers for our unresolved childhood traumas.

Remember, anything that is a symptom is an idiot light. Even triggers, as well as emotions, are idiot lights.

Here's an example: In Traditional Chinese Medicine, the liver is related to anger or frustration and tastes sour. An alcoholic chooses alcohol because it's metabolized in the liver to stuff the emotion of anger/frustration, so they drink to "relax." Many alcoholics have experienced childhood traumas over which they had no control. As adults, the conscious mind (inner child) wants to suppress the unresolved emotion, so it chooses foods or drinks to suppress.

The reply going through your head right now is, "But I'm not angry." You totally missed the word *suppress* .... So some of the liver's idiot lights are acid reflux, sour burping, sighing, pain in the rib cage, migraines, or stabbing fixed pains -- as well as anger or frustration.

Another example of suppressed anger is with breast cancer. In Traditional Chinese Medicine, two meridians run through the breast. One is the Spleen meridian, which is connected to the emotion pensiveness/thoughtlessness, and the other is the Liver, which is connected to the emotion anger/frustration. The breast represents the nourishment between mother and child, and when that bond is broken, we stuff the emotions with the wrong foods, which help grow the cancers. I have seen many adoptees and birth moms who develop breast cancer, some metastasize to the liver, which is one of the most severe bond breakages between mother and child.

The liver has over 400 functions, and since it doesn't need any more, it's essential to love your liver. Many of the foods we eat are metabolized in the liver, such as proteins, fats, hormones, and sugars. When we eat meat and dairy, the proteins, fats, hormones, and DNA are almost bio-identical to our bodies. The cells in your body think that you're eating your own tissue. Your body says, "Hey, I know where this cell goes," so it stores it in the most likable compartment. Cells are like for like.

A good example is dairy products, because from the body's viewpoint, it thinks your drinking your own breast milk. For men, it will go to the prostate and the chest. Hormone-related cells will be attracted to hormone-related tissues, so the body will store these cells in the breast tissue where it thinks the dairy originated from.

Have you ever wondered why so many people drink alcohol with meats or fish? It's because the meat, with all of the proteins and fats, is so hard for the liver to process, it will make you crave a relaxant such as alcohol, which makes sugar in the liver. The sugar helps the liver relax, but it's not what the liver wanted and so it puts even more stress on the organ. Some meat-eaters wear a lot of cologne because they can't smell it. The body starts to produce ammonia because of the meat, increasing body odor and reducing their sense of smell.

Foods that will create problems for the liver are: meats, eggs, dairy, alcohol, drugs that are metabolized in the liver, and processed sugars.

Food the liver loves: Green leafy veggies, barley, wheat, quinoa, cabbage, parsley, sour or fermented foods such as pickles, umeboshi plums, and sauerkraut.

I have seen many people crave sour pickles to help stimulate the liver's energy to help ease unresolved anger/frustration, and aid digestion. A friend of mine was abused as a child and worked for a pickle company for many years. There were several jars of sour pickles in the refrigerator and saved the jars for storage. I used to eat mustard sandwiches, containing vinegar and a ton of spinach with vinegar. And I usually ate a whole jar of pickles and drank the juice in one sitting to help me counterbalance the stress at home as a child. I also spent many hours in the wood, which is the element of the liver.

According to TCM, to help the liver heal, it's important to understand the nature of the liver's energy, which is constantly moving and growing. The liver element is wood or tree energy, which is continually moving and growing and providing oxygen to the body. Take a walk-in nature and breathe the air that trees provide. When we eat green leafy veggies, chlorophyll helps us re-oxygenate the cells.

The companion to the liver is the gall bladder, which is also wood energy, but the emotion is different. It's responsible for worry. Think about how many people have their gall bladders removed, as they literally try to cut out the worry from their lives rather than seek to understand the reasons behind the worry.

Spleen, stomach, and pancreas are connected to the earth element, the taste of sweet, and the emotions pensiveness/thoughtlessness. How many times have you stuffed your face with chocolate, sweets, cookies, ice cream, or cake -- to make everything feel better? But then we might have a temporary chocolate or sugar high, but eventually, we'll come crashing down, because sugar is a depressant. Many of us crave the taste of sweets, and yet we have no idea what sweet foods really are...... they're not chocolate. We choose foods that taste sweet, such as sugar or fake sugar-sweetened foods that kill all the digestive enzymes in the gut. Sugar will kill the enzymes within 72 hours; then we can no longer absorb the proper nutrition from the foods we are eating. This is where all of our problems start, in the gut. If we eat foods that create acid and deprive us of oxygen, we will become sick.

There is a quote attributed to Jesus in the book *The Gnostic Gospels* by Elaine Pagles:

"If you bring forth what is within you, what you bring forth will save you. If you do not bring forth what is within you, then what you do not bring forth will destroy you."

CHAPTER 8

Rejection

Let's talk about heart transplants. Many people in the U.S. receive heart transplants, and must take anti-rejection medication; otherwise, their body's immune system will fight and reject the new heart. Even though the cells in your heart are identical, your DNA is not, unless you're an identical twin. Now, let's think about this: we have a heart, and we get a new heart that has the same proteins, fats, hormones, and can work exactly like the heart it replaces. But, if the DNA is not the same as the previous heart, the new heart gets rejected. The heart alone consists of billions and billions of cells; that's why our bodies reject heart transplants so quickly.

Cancer cells, which are transformed over time, don't show up on a scan until there are over a million of them. If you go out to dinner and have a wonderful meal, look at your plate and ask yourself: How many items there contain unhealthy proteins, fats and hormones......and animal DNA? What if we ate a plate of unhealthy proteins, fats, hormones, and animal DNA every day? What would happen inside our bodies with this daily cell transplant? Hmmm... REJECTION!

Just like an organ transplant, our body's immune system would naturally start to reject these foreign cells because the DNA is NOT OURS! But this process takes time, so the body ends up storing the new found animal cells in the body. This is why so many people gain weight. In plants, the DNA looks so foreign that the body rejects the cells quickly. It will speed up our metabolism because the body wants to eliminate those cells as fast as possible. Your intestines are only designed to hold 2-3 meals.

Since our bodies are such efficient machines, the "garbage men" of the body you're your immune system, which contains your white blood cells, will start to gather up the animal DNA or "not so like cells" into neat little piles. That's what we call cancer. Some cancers can take up to 30 years to show up on a scan, even before patients have symptoms. But the symptoms that we ignore are like the idiot lights in your car; you don't know what it means, but the warning light is on.

Every time you eat a meal, the idiot light can go on. Ever feel gassy, bloated, acid reflux, congestion in your throat, nose running, tired or lethargic, maybe you cough or sneeze while eating, or you have to use the restroom after you eat? These symptoms are your body's immune system kicking into high gear; you ate something that's causing an autoimmune response. After you eat, you should feel satisfied to the point where you could either run a mile or sleep comfortably. Having no symptoms after you eat means you ate the right foods.

Now in TCM, food is considered a medicine. The Five Elements: Earth, fire, water, metal, and wood are each connected to a taste: Sweet, bitter, salty, pungent, or sour. Those tastes are connected to the body's organ system and body tissues, using those foods as healing medicine.

Genesis 1:29 in the Bible says: **"And God said, Behold, I have given you every herb-bearing seed, which is upon the face of all the earth, and every tree, in which is the fruit of a tree-yielding seed; to you, it shall be for meat."**

Sorry folks, he wasn't kidding when he said that, for thousands of years, people all over the world have turned to plants to heal themselves. But somehow, over our years of what we call progression (often, in actuality, regression), we have disconnected from Mother Earth and have gone astray.

We no longer know what to cook or how to cook it, or what to eat to be healthy. We don't even know the simple remedies like eating ginger for a tummy ache, or what's locally grown, or in season. Didn't you ever wonder why ginger is always served with sushi or fish in Asian restaurants? Because it's the antidote for seafood poisoning. Why is daikon radish always served with tempura? Because radish breaks down fats, so you don't feel heavy, bloated, and sluggish after you eat. What about cinnamon? Why do we commonly eat it in the wintertime? Because it has a warming property and helps fight off colds. Somehow over the years, we have lost our food common sense, and have become disconnected from our bodies.

"Why aren't we our own best and most loving friend? Who's going to *love* us and care for us if we don't do it ourselves? Who knows us the best, and has our best interests at heart? We are the love we seek!"

In the Bible quote from Corinthians 1:13, verse 5, this stands out:

"Love is patient, love is kind. It does not envy; it does not boast; it is not proud. It does not dishonor others; it is not self-seeking, it is not easily angered, it keeps no record of wrongs."

Wait! What? Love is NOT self-seeking? We, as humans, are always self-seeking! What's in it for me? We forget that we are the love and the light we seek in others. We each are all the love that we could ever need or want. If we think like humans and forget that our light being, spirit, or Holy Spirit self even exists, we'll be stuck at what I call "The Five Elements Human Pity Party." The lowly human experience. The victim. Poor, pitiful me.

So let's say God, or whatever name you choose, does exist. In quantum physics, the only place for something similar to exist would be in the 11th dimension where there is a theory called -- for M, Mother, magical. This is where what theology would call omnipotent events happen. A magical place of good vibrations that occur anytime, anywhere, anyplace, all at the same time. The 11th dimension is everywhere, including inside you. Since you can't be disconnected, that means you're blocking that dimension, denying part of yourself. Why?

An online article called "Blue Brain Team Discovers a Multi-Dimensional Universe in Brain Networks" was on eurekalert.org, June 12, 2017. Henry Markram from the EPFL institute in Switzerland stated, "We found a world that we had never imagined. There are tens of millions of these objects, even in a small speck of the brain, up to seven dimensions. In some networks, we found structures with up to eleven dimensions."

An online article in the *New York Post* written by Michael Blaustein, printed June 13, 2017, "The Human Brain Sees the World as an 11-Dimensional Multiverse," states: "New research suggests that the human brain is almost beyond comprehension. Because it doesn't process the world in two dimensions or even three; no, the human brain understands the visual world in up to 11 different dimensions."

We as humans have the ability in our brains to operate at the 11th dimension. Surprise! Not really. You've always known this, but you've never thought about it. Remember that gut feeling or intuition you've had? What about that little voice that gives you incredible, spot-on guiding information? What about when God spoke to Jesus? Or when you talk to your dead relatives?

So why is all of this so important when we look at diseases such as cancer? Because cancer puts out a vibration, just as your body does. And conditions such as cancer lower your vibrational frequency. When we vibrate at a lower frequency, we get sick and dimmish our connection to God and the Universe, and we become emotionally disconnected. So every time you eat something that contains unhealthy proteins, fats, hormones, and animal DNA, the body's immune system kicks in and lowers your vibrational frequency, from healthy to sick. Over time, our system becomes weaker from the abuse, and starts to break down, which increases the risk of disease. That's why it's vitally important to feed your body medicine in the form of healthy foods to help heal and repair itself and increase our vibrational frequency. If everything in the universe is vibrating, is it healthy and healing, or destructive? Is your tv, phone, microwave or computer putting out a healthy vibrational frequency, or is it better for you to sit near a tree or the ocean? These are the laws of nature to for which we are bound.

Remember Newton's 3rd Law of Physics: "For every action, there is an equal and opposite reaction." We are part of the whole universe, God, Higher Power -- whether we like it or not. There is no pill or safe house that can distance us from that. We just have to face facts. We are part of the Universe. Most of your body is comprised of s the most common elements in the universe: oxygen, hydrogen, nitrogen, and carbon. You can't get away. You're as much a part of the universe as it is of you. You're 96% of the Universe. That means mom and dad only contributed 4% of you.

In John Bradshaw's book *The Family: A Revolutionary Way of Self Discovery*, "Cancer, it has been discovered, correlates with emotional repressions." He goes on to talk about how children develop and see the world and their parents. "Children parent themselves the way they were parented. If the child got shamed for feeling angry, sad, or sexual, they would shame themselves each time they feel angry, sad, or sexual. All of their feelings, needs, and drives become shame-bound. The inner self-rupture is so painful, the child must develop a 'false self.' This false self is manifested in a masked or rigid role, either determined by culture or by the family system's needs for balance. Over time the child identifies with the false self and becomes totally unconscious of their own true feelings, needs, and wants. The shame is internalized. Shame is no longer a feeling; it's an identity. The real self has withdrawn from conscious contact."

I recently had the opportunity to read David Clark's book, *Broken Open.* He wrote: "Somewhere along the way, addicts forget everything except pain. Pain becomes the only thing we see. And we see it in everything. Work, friends, life, *love* all of it -- just pain in disguise. As a survival mechanism, we learn to eat the pain for breakfast; we even use pain to fuel the one thing that makes us feel good--drinking or using. But by the time we figure out that the alcohol is making the pain worse, we can't imagine living in a world that doesn't have the only solid thing we know in it." His pain became his fuel to become an ultra-marathon runner. He was formerly obese and addicted to alcohol, until he turned to running. His pattern of dysfunction goes from childhood into his running years. And even though he was a successful runner, running was addictive and a form of self-abuse, a pattern he was never able to break. At the age of 49, he died from complications of herniated disc surgery. The spine (bone/kidney) in TCM is related to the emotion fear, and the lack of feeling emotionally or physically supported, and to our essence, from our parents.

I bring up this quote because we as children are dependent on our parents or caregivers. It's part of our survival to ensure that we're not abandoned, and fear is a driving factor in these instincts. Fear can keep us safe, or it can be highly irrational. As children, we learn early on how to mimic our parents to survive, but in doing so, we pick up their patterns of behaviors from their own childhood traumas that were unresolved. We pick up their subconscious coping skills and incorporate them into our struggles, thus making sure we aren't abandoned by our broken caregivers.

Addiction comes in many forms: HEALTH ISSUES, behavioral, friends, sports, weight, image, relationship, drugs, sex, abuse. When we learn these issues from the people we needed most in order to survive, we subconsciously believe it's *love*. We think that *love* keeps us safe from being abandoned, and we can share our pain, misery, and fear with our parents. Until we recognize these patterns, we hold onto them as if they are indeed ourselves—our very identity. The group we belong to in order to ensure our survival, not out of *love* but out of the survival instinct, and fear. They are not who we are or represent the love we generate for ourselves.

Health issues can become addictive and reflect the emotional pain we haven't overcome. TCM puts all the pieces together: mind-body and spirit.

CHAPTER 9

Limbic System and Mirroring Neurons

Limbic System:

Known as the reptilian brain, it's responsible for fight, flight, or freezing, and affects emotions, long-term memories, arousal, motivation, and smell. This is the area of the brain that keeps us safe from danger. When activated, many physiological responses happen in the endocrine system and the autonomic nervous system. The reptilian brain is also responsible for sexual arousal and the "high" we feel after some activities, taking drugs, or eating sugars like lactose. The limbic system also works with other systems in the brain, such as the basal ganglia, which is responsible for posture and movement and maintains dopamine levels (our feel-good drug). It is also connected with the prefrontal cortex, which is responsible for emotional problem solving. This system can be activated at any time, for any situation, known or unknown, in which the body feels attacked. As children, this situation will more than likely be triggered out of fear. These activations happen frequently when we are young, as we learn about the world around us. Children cannot distinguish what they should be fearful of until they experience it.

In many cases, as adults, an experience that seems so trivial to us can seem catastrophic to a child. Have you ever seen a child cry so hard that they tremble? Or, what about when we have a good scare or a near car accident, and we are shaking? Or when a patient is just out of surgery, and trembles uncontrollably? Or a Parkinson's patient? Spiders, snakes, or mice. That's when the limbic system gets activated. The tremor is the way the body naturally resets the limbic system, along with emotional problem-solving. When we can look back at a situation and emotionally problem-solve it, or look at the issue from a different perspective, we can finally see what happened and realize that we survived the crisis. It's essential to see what happened and understand why, so we can begin to heal and release traumatic events.

When I was in kindergarten, we were going on a field trip to the fire station. I was so scared and crying that I couldn't go, so I stayed behind with a teacher. When I went to hypnosis school, this experience came up, and I started crying because the fear came back. When the instructor asked if I was okay, I started laughing, saying, "Yes, I got my fire hat and badge." As I think about it, the element fire is connected to the heart and the emotion joy/ love in Traditional Chinese Medicine. At the time, my parents were living apart; my father was an alcoholic. Within the year, my father killed himself.

At the age of 29, I had a bad car accident; I was in a lot of pain; my heart was out of rhythm, and my body was shaking for weeks. I was hit from behind; the Universe or God was sending me the message to go forward in my life. That push along the way helped me get back into school and away from my unhealthy marriage. The accident was what I needed to grow forward in a healthy and healing way. Unfortunately, we can retain traumas deep within ourselves, and may not even realize that they are there. When triggered by a smell, location, sight, sound, or emotion, they can evoke an unresolved response, which will reactivate the fight, flight, or freezing response, or PTSD. We will feel our heart race, feel sick to our stomach, hyper-vigilant (on edge), resort to an angry or violent response, may want to run away, or just curl up in a ball and want to be comforted.

As we get older, we move away from people with broken patterns. Then we begin to get glimpses of our past and awaken to the truth. We start the healing process slowly and naturally. Many people, however, remain stuck in these unresolved traumas and hold onto them for several reasons: out of what we perceive as *love,* or the fear of abandonment, guilt, or shame, which continue to have a grip on so many people. We learn unhealthy coping skills, such as unhealthy eating, drug or alcohol addiction, bad relationships, abuse, porn, rape, incest, verbal abuse. On vacation, I met a successful businessman. As we were talking, he told me he had a fetish: he likes to spend an hour occasionally with a woman who beat him. So I asked him, "Did your mom ever beat you?" And he quickly replied, "Yes." Clearly, he was re-enacting his trauma with his mother; the fetish was a symbol of his "*loving*" bond with her. He had no idea that that was the real meaning behind what he was doing. I finally saw the light bulb go off in his head.

We start to open our eyes slowly with small coincidences, something you heard or saw, or a situation in your life that gives you a short glimpse of your past. These truths are there to help you explore and heal; they are not there to harm you or make you feel bad. But if you do feel something negative, take deep breaths and ask yourself, "Have I ever felt this way before? Have I ever seen this before? Have I ever heard this before?" Then, we can begin to see the patterns for what they are, a reflection of unresolved pain. These unresolved traumas may be so deep, you may not even be aware of them. But they are there, and so is the disease, the latent unresolved trauma that has festered for years. Every disease has an unresolved emotion, and every emotion has an unresolved illness. Those are the laws of nature, plain and simple physics.

Mirror Neurons:

These allow us to imitate body language, facial expressions, and emotions related to the empathic, social, and other behaviors essential for our survival and social life. They allow us to establish trust and enable us to drop our energy so we can begin to feel comfortable with other people. It's part of our survival, and we adapt to fit in so that no one will abandon us. In other words, they're our "monkey see -- monkey do" neurons that drive our basic survival instinct. Oh, good, -- so if our caregivers are pessimistic, angry, depressed, violent, or abandoned, our mirror neurons will activate and mimic these behaviors -- whether consciously or subconsciously. So that we can live someone else's emotions instead. It's why we leave one toxic pattern for another.

CHAPTER 10

Emotional Factors to Consider

Like You, Like Me:

Oh, the mirroring neurons! They are necessary for our survival, BUT they are a double-edged sword. When we are under the age of 15 these neurons are very active, because we need this ability to mimic or fit in with whoever is helping us survive. Remember the story of the "Little Jungle Boy?" How he mimicked the animals to survive? Well, guess what, you've done the same. If we fit in, then we won't get abandoned; we'll thrive and survive. How did it feel when you were a kid, and you were told to do something? If you didn't do it, you were afraid that something would happen, and maybe -- just maybe -- you would get in trouble or, even worse, be abandoned. During our development as children, there are ages where we can feel personally responsible, like for raising our siblings, or even for the break-up of our parents. So what's the deal with the mirroring neurons? It's the same thing as imprinting in animals. Let's say your dad *loves* the

Boston Red Sox, and you want your dad to *love* and accept you. So your mirroring neurons kick in, and unless what, you now love the Red Sox!

But how does all of this affect cancer?

Well, let's say that mommy had a lousy childhood and never got therapy, and that when she was under a lot of stress (pain), she wanted comfort food such as ice cream (pleasure)to help ease her (pain). (Addiction). Now that mommy is feeling comforted (really, it's her hurt inner child), and she wants to share in her pleasure with baby (you), so now baby feels (pleasure) with mommy. (Addiction buddies) equals *LOVE*. The brain is saying that addiction equals *love*, pain, pleasure, and survival. What could be so wrong? When we leave home as wounded children, we will seek out the same pattern until we recognize it and heal from it. How many times have you heard people say,

"I married my mother" ...or... "I married my father."

Losing the Baby Status:

Have you ever watched those videos of parents who filmed their kids when they tell them they're going to be a big brother or sister, and then the kid has an absolute meltdown? And will say, "I don't want to be a big brother!" Or "Why are you having another kid?" Or they seem to pummel or torture their little brother or sister...This is the child's emotional grief and sadness reaction when they are no longer number one in the family; their inner child feels abandoned, not good enough, or replaced. They lost the "baby status."

An online article in *Parents' Magazine* called "Big-Sibling Blues," June 30, 2014, by Renee Bacher, states: "But it can be an emotionally rough road to become a big brother or sister before the age of 2." The article continues, "This is by far the hardest time for the firstborn to accept a new baby," says Fran Walfish, Psy.D., author of *The Self-Aware Parent.* "Every child needs a full tablespoon of Mommy all to herself. Two years is a full tablespoon. Less than that can increase sibling jealousy and resistance to accepting the baby as a full member of the family. If your older child doesn't seem visibly upset by the baby's arrival, it's possible that she is still grieving the end of the way her life used to be. Often this grief doesn't show up as overt jealousy and tantrums, until the baby becomes mobile and starts grabbing your older child's things."

There are many cases of this reaction at any age. Other contributing factors are involved when a mother has a baby, such as moving, a change in family dynamics, or any additional stress that the family goes through that affects the child.

Mother's Guilt:

In an article from the *Huffington Post* called "How to Deal with Mother's Guilt," by Mia Redrick, dated 11/29/2011: "Mother's guilt is real. Nearly all of us experience it. We are racked with guilt, feeling that our best isn't good enough. We struggle when work commitments prevent us from attending school events, and we are crushed by the looks of disappointment on our children's faces. We wonder if choices we have made, such as what school to send our kids to, have not had far-reaching negative consequences, and if a different path would have resulted in happier, more well-adjusted kids. We moms might feel guilty when we can't afford something for our kids or have the nagging feeling that we simply don't spend enough time with them.  Mother's guilt is only natural, and is the consequence of wanting to be a good mother to your children. However, in the end, it will only weigh you down."

I know that my mom had a lot of guilt and struggled. She had to endure placing my brother in the state mental institution, and later, went into one herself when I was still young. She compensated for her frustrations by binge eating until she threw up; or else she went shopping and bought me too much stuff, which then caused her checks to bounce.

Our Mother and Her Hurt Inner Child:

We all want the perfect mother. But her life's journey was based on the struggles that she faced from her parents and unresolved traumas. They're many reasons our mothers can't raise us like we imagined or needed, which leaves us longing for her emotional and physical care. We as children cannot see the emotionally stunted or traumatized mother who has been frozen in time at the age of her trauma. I have heard many stories from women who have had physically or sexually abused mothers, fondled or molested, adoptees or birth moms who have passed down to the next generation these unresolved traumas. Unfortunately, many of these women never got professional help or emotional support to help resolve these traumas. Even my mom had her issues with my grandmother, who was 32 years old and a successful theater actress when my mom came along. She made it clear to my mother that "she had ruined her career."

When a Parent Becomes Sick

On a GoFundMe page, Shannon Tynan stated, "Whether it's a stroke, a bad fall, breast cancer, or an incurable rare skin disease" -- when a parent becomes sick, "your life instantly changes." You're forced to grow up in ways that you never imagined. "Suddenly, you find yourself on an emotional roller coaster—one second, you feel angry; the next, overwhelmed, stressed, or upset. All of these reactions are instinctual and natural. Dealing with" --a sick parent is difficult, -- "and no matter what people tell you or what you read any article, it's hard to actually prepare."

As a child, there's great fear when a parent is sick; you start to wonder if they're going to die. Therefore, in many cases, there is no convincing otherwise in a child's mind. I wasn't raised with grandparents or aunts and uncles, and my father had killed himself in his early 50s. As a child, I had a fear that older people (meaning, in their 50s) were suddenly going to drop dead. Your imagination can be a powerful thing, and it can be just as convincing to someone who has trauma.

Family Legacy

What is your family's legacy? Is there drug or alcohol addiction, depression, physical or mental abuse, workaholism, control issues, obesity, gas-lighting, anger, guilt, shame, or abandonment? Do you want to repeat these? Many of us repeat these negative patterns, or seek them out in relationships, but these are choices that we make to display our *love* for our parents or caretakers. Are these the patterns you want to show your friends, family, or significant other? If we see these legacies as traumatic patterns, then we can learn to let them go. As you reflect on your life, you'll see that you've picked up many of these patterns, and that you've been living out your family history. But is this truly who you are, and who you want to be? Are these burdens necessary for you to carry? Do you need them to live the life that you dreamed of? **Reflect, and then let go......**

If we don't explore, we can't grow forward in our lives. The *love* we seek and deserve will be forever falling from our grasp because we have failed to give it to ourselves. How much suffering are you willing to have in your life? Take the time to learn the reasons behind your struggles. Are they truly yours, or just a pattern you learned, which you identify as *love*?

We'll always be connected to the outer world in some way, shape, or form, but are you interconnected with your mind, body, and spirit? Do you genuinely feel at home within yourself? Or have you abandoned yourself?

You choose how you live, so choose what brings you peace and contentment in your life.

> **"I know what I really want for Christmas, I want my childhood back. Nobody is going to give me that....I know it doesn't make sense, but since when is Christmas about sense, anyway? It is about a child of long ago and far away, and it is about the child of now. In you and me. Waiting behind the door of our hearts for something wonderful to happen."**
> **Robert Fulghum -- *All I Really Need to Know, I Learned in Kindergarten***
>
> **"The person...in the grip of an old distress says things that are not pertinent, does things that don't work, fails to cope with the situation, and endures terrible feelings that have nothing to do with the present."**
> **Harvey Jackins – Founder of Re-Evaluation Counseling**

In the book *In the Realm of a Hungry Ghost* by Dr. Gabor Mate, states, "The neurobiology of addiction in a nutshell. Attacking energy, expressed tantrums or aggression, rapidly erupts from a young child because the brain circuits that would allow him to resolve his frustrations in other ways are as yet formed. The impulse-control circuitry isn't connected yet, either." He also stated, "The three environmental conditions absolutely essential to optimal human brain development are nutrition, physical security and consistent emotional nurturing......The importance of this point cannot be overstated: Emotional nurturance is an absolute requirement for healthy neurobiological brain development.... The child needs to be in an attachment relationship with at least one reliably available, protective, and psychologically present and reasonably non-stressed adult." Another quote in the book, from Dr. Vincent Felitti, --Internal medical doctor who specializes in childhood trauma stated, "The cause of addiction is predominantly experience-dependent during childhood..."

Meanwhile, our simple attachment to breast milk or dairy becomes our survival addiction...

CHAPTER 11

Milk and Hormones

Breast milk is our very first addiction. It doesn't matter if the milk comes from a human or an animal, because it contains tryptophan and lactose. The tryptophan keeps us sedated, and the lactose or sugar acts like cocaine in the brain. It's the reason why babies sleep after feeding and why they cry mercilessly for more milk. Breast-feeding is an addiction for both mother and child. It's about survival and thriving. We see this pattern of behavior again and again: Candy, chocolate, fancy coffees and lattes, ice cream, cakes, and cookies. Even when people drink alcohol, the liver metabolizes it into sugar. Sugar, or a more potent form of sweetener, is in just about any kind of food that has been processed. It is also responsible for inflammation in the body.

Any milk from humans or animals contains these common ingredients: Protein, tryptophan, casein, whey, fat, carbohydrates, water, and ash -- and this is where our body gets into trouble. There are differences in the amounts of these ingredients from animal to human. And in the DNA, the differences cause an autoimmune reaction.

Lactose and the Brain:

Lactose, the sugar found in milk, hits the receptors on the tongue, which activates the brain's reward system. Overconsumption of any form of sugar will cause a loss of control, or cravings. Dopamine is part of the brain's reward system, and sugar causes dopamine to be released, which is necessary for motivation, mental or physical energy. Sugar doesn't have as strong an effect on the brain's dopamine receptors as cocaine, but it's a similar process, and can become just as addictive as any drug.

When the receptors are negatively affected, it can cause a person to "not follow the rules" that affect memory and the ability to learn. It also affects other parts of the brain that signal the gut to feel full. When we over-consume sugar, both the body and the brain will suffer from inflammation-causing depression, and other diseases, such as cancers.

Estrogen

This is a hormone that contributes to the production of milk. The amount of estrogen differs in dairy, and the products that are low in fat will have the highest estrogen content. People trying to avoid unhealthy fats consume low-fat yogurt, cottage cheese, milk, and ice cream, and so over half of the breast cancers found in the milk ducts are estrogen-positive. The majority of the population is allergic to dairy; symptoms can range from runny nose, congestion in the throat, gas or bloat, diarrhea or constipation, to Crohn's disease, endometriosis, and the formation of cancers.

Progesterone

When cows produce milk with higher fat content, the progesterone will also increase, especially when processed into butter, cheese, cream cheese, sour cream, and other high-fat products. This extra fat content may contribute to fatty breast tissue and the formation of estrogen-negative breast cancers.

Oxytocin

Affectionately called the "cuddle hormone" or "love hormone," oxytocin is activated during labor, helps brighten the mother's mood and increases her need to nurture her infant. As the mother starts to breastfeed, oxytocin is activated; some mothers experience a euphoric or orgasmic-like state when breastfeeding. This helps the baby feel calm because of their hormonal reaction when cuddled and breastfeeding and tryptophan and lactose in the breast milk. As the mother and child begin to bond while breastfeeding, oxytocin increases the brain's opioid system increasing the feeling of *love* in the mother as well as the infant through the milk. The mothers feel the "high of the opioids, which increases her desire to nurture, bond, and *love* the infant. This bond is so vital in the child's first few years of their lives, and that's why they act so inconsolable when mom is away because they are running on a steady stream of endorphins and this "high" keeps them growing and exploring.

When we're children, if our mothers are under stress, or in emotional or physical pain, or just unavailable, our brain's opioid system is still activated. So we'll seek an alternative to help release our endorphins to "self-soothe."

One of the best alternatives to breast milk is dairy products—nature's perfect little drug.

As adults, when these endorphins are activated, we seek an emotional attachment in relationships, such as family or partners, for the physical and emotional connections we call *love*. In the brain, *love*, pleasure, and pain are intrinsically tied together. In other words, "*love* hurts." When we think about an intimate relationship, it will be the closest to mimicking the experience of the bond between mother and child.

Dairy it's everywhere! Some of the surprising foods that contain some ingredient or form of dairy such as: casein, whey, milk, butter, or cheese, are in products: Lactaid, salad dressings, sherbet, tuna fish, shellfish, vitamins, medications, gum, custards, flavored potato chips, and deli meats.

Estrogen Blockers

Estrogen blockers are usually prescribed for 5 to 7 years; some patients may experience a reoccurrence of cancers after finishing the medication. Reoccurrence can occur because many of the patients are still consuming dairy products; while they are on the drug, it will block the estrogen from the dairy products. Once off the estrogen blocker the dairy's estrogen is no longer blocked. Our bodies will identify the estrogen from the dairy as its own cells, causing the body to store these dairy cells in the breast. This maybe the reason why so many women have a reoccurrence of breast cancer. I have seen these reoccurrences in women who continue to eat dairy.

CHAPTER 12

Our Survival Mode

Protection to Stay Innocent

One of the most challenging jobs a human being has is raising a child. Because of your specific life experiences, you never really know how this experience will affect someone else, let alone a child. Parents do their best to protect their children from traumatic events, but things slip through the cracks. Exposure to certain events too soon can negatively alter a child's behavior. These traumatic or shocking moments get burned into our brains and set us up for our fear-based survival skills to kick in.

I grew up in a small town. There were about two and a half TV channels to watch, but I can vividly remember scenes from the Vietnam War and the shocking pictures in *Life* magazine. They affected me, and probably my father, who served in the Army during WWII and killed himself when I was 6. These scenarios set up my fear of people in uniform and were reinforced when I visited my brother David in the state mental institution. My child self always considered people in uniform as damaged, capable of doing scary, irrational things.

Patients at the state mental institution were dressed in white uniforms and had close-shaven heads; my brother was so stressed out there that he would often punch himself in the head. At the time, I believed that the purple mark on his temple was permanent. To add to the creepiness of it all, they made David wear a helmet to keep him from beating his head against the wall.

I'm sure that my mom was just as traumatized, because I know she was riddled with guilt for having him placed in the institution. During the '60s, parents with a doctor's consultation decided that it was best for someone to be "committed" to a state mental institution. The parents had to "sign the child over to the state." That meant that my parents gave up their rights to their firstborn -- this was while my mother was eight months pregnant with me. It was just like the movie "One Flew Over the Cuckoo's Nest," which came out when I was 11 years old. Yes, as a kid, I saw it, and lived it.

My mother was diagnosed as manic-depressive (of course) when I was a child. She had placed her son, whom she couldn't ever get back, into a mental institution. Her husband of over 20 years killed himself six years later. This left her with four kids and no new income. At times she herself was in a mental institution, "to get better." For the most part, when she came home, she was a *loving* and kind woman -- doing her best with the hand she was dealt. When her "lithium" level was off, she would do bizarre things -- such as putting on her bra over her nightgown or using three different cups to try to make one cup of coffee.

On one occasion, she woke up in the middle of the night and was screaming my name out the front door, looking for me. Another time I can remember, again in the middle of the night, she called the police, telling them that Charles Manson was coming to kill her - this was after she read the book *Helter Skelter*. Needless to say, I had trouble sleeping as a child, and was always wary of people who drank or took any medications. For me, there was always some sort of trauma or drama -- both at home and school. My salvation was in riding my bike and hiking for hours in the woods.

Living in the Box

We all know the rules and regulations of "living in the box." We're well aware of what we can or cannot do, and what we can or cannot say, to stay safe and out of trouble. The "walls of the box" are created out of shame, guilt, fear, or abandonment as we desperately try to "fit in." As children, we need our dysfunctional families for survival, but as hard as we try to fit in, we lose part of ourselves in the process. This box is created from various elements: stares, like the look of death, abuse both physically, mentally or sexual screaming, yelling, anger, fear, and addiction to name a few.

As a result, it causes us as children to stay silent, adhere to time constraints, not making noise, looking a certain way or wearing certain clothes, anything to keep the peace in order to make our parents happy and not lash out at us. We want to be on our best behavior because we want to be *loved,* and we want to fit in, in order not to be rejected or abandoned by our caretakers. We do it at home, at work, with our parents, spouses, friends, wherever we feel we have to conform to fit in. It's part of our survival mechanism. We first learn how to do this from whoever raised us from birth until about 15. We need them to survive, so we start to mimic their behavior -- out of fear of abandonment and whatever we think at the time is *love*. We just want to be *loved,* and to fit in; but then bits and pieces of ourselves are lost and forgotten…until we have the opportunity to move away, or someone dies, or we come to our own spiritual awakening.

We want to stay in our caretaker's "good graces," so we begin to mimic their behavior or behaviors. A good example is learning to be a healthy chef, be involved in meditation, creative art, or anything else that makes our *soul* feel good and gives us a sense of fulfillment and healing. But our caretakers had their traumas. And most of them never went to counseling or healed from these deep wounds, they pass them on subconsciously. I have met people who were raised by mothers who've been sexually abused, only to be attracted to partners who were sexually abused. When we don't heal, our natural healthy behaviors change into unhealthy patterns, and then everyone who spends time with us will pick up on these patterns.

Think about your family's traumas, whether alcoholism, drug, sexual, physical, or mental abuse, death or illnesses, abandonment, guilt or shame, then take a good look at the backstories of the people who are closest to you. The laws of nature are about survival, and to survive, we must fit in or be left out, and in nature, being left out often leads to death. One of our strongest instincts is to fit in. This type of toxic situation kicks us into survival mode, just to make it through our childhood. Somehow, our brain associates this with *love,* but in actuality, it's not! We are all, however, just doing our best to survive our childhood.

One of the reactions to fitting in is that we develop covert skills. We use our newfound stealth to do all those questionable acts without anyone knowing. This is our form of acting out. Oftentimes it can be directed at the person with whom we have the most issues, or someone the same sex as that person.

As we move away from these people and start to get a glimmer of reality, we begin to discover, or awaken to, the truth. It's easy for an adult to say, "Well, my childhood wasn't that bad," but when we discount the pain we felt as a child, we abandon our hurt "inner child." Remember all the times you cried yourself to sleep, scared, with a headache or a tummy ache, or you went to sleep wishing or hoping that mommy or daddy would do_______________? Yes, we all have those moments. What about remembering your childhood? Some people have blocked out the bad parts, simply in order to cope. For example, there have been many documented cases of sexual abuse that the victims could not even remember happening.

The part of the brain that tries to keep us safe is called the limbic system, which is responsible for fight, flight, or freezing, or PTSD. Part of PTSD is denial, which would account for memory loss or memory protection. I often consult with people who can't remember months or years of their childhood. That's usually where the traumas or events are hiding.

I have seen women who've had gynecological cancers which, from my experience, might have formed, because of emotions that have been blocked due to sexual abuse, rape, or fondling. These cancers are in the Sacral chakra, which is related to the kidney in Traditional Chinese Medicine. The kidney is linked to the emotion of fear as well as essence we inherit from our parents, sex or sexuality. Many of these women can't remember parts of their childhood, which we spend time openly discussing. Therapies are available that help a person safely recall blocked trauma and emotions: inner child work, somatic therapy, hypnosis, research, tapping, EMDR can all help assist a person in the healing process from unresolved traumas.

> **"The mind, once enlightened, cannot again become dark."**
> **Thomas Paine – Political Activist**

Push Away

So why do people push away? Although there are many reasons, none of them have to do with you. Yes, I think you're special, but the reality is you can't make people feel anything. People choose to feel. The first type of push-away I like to call the "Lifeguard Move." You are the lifeguard, and you see a swimmer in trouble, whether emotional or physical, and you swim out to rescue them. You realize that their behavior is so desperate, they're trying to drown you.

The number one lesson in being a lifeguard is to guard your own life.

When any lifeguard rescues a victim, who grabs and clings to the lifeguard, the first rule is to push the victim away because they will drown themselves, and you, in the process. So, the next time you meet someone who's worthy of your exceptional rescuing skills......run! Of course, you can always throw them a pool noodle, but why, since they didn't even go to the dollar store to buy their own pool noodle -- to rescue themselves.

Remember, actions speak louder than words.

The second lesson is the "Leach Move." Those suckers will bleed you dry. Yes, they can seem warm and fuzzy at first, but the reality is that you must see past the package and do some investigative work. These are the ME, ME, ME people who think that whatever happened to them when they were growing up, now they deserve everything good. They are incapable of having a balanced relationship with themselves, let alone anyone else.

Don't attempt to change these people. They're perfect the way they are. They're not perfect for you, and that's okay.

There are billions of people; out there, and several are the right ones for you, who will encourage you to grow and heal every day. You can have a grownup conversation with them, without judgment or ridicule, just compassion and understanding. Above all, trust your intuition. **If you feel uncomfortable or nauseated or emptiness, guilt or shame around these people, then run.**

Compassion is one of the hardest lessons to learn, because it requires you to love unconditionally which our parents never taught us, because they themselves were probably in survival mode. However, the more you begin to tune into yourself and your true feelings, the more you can be compassionate to others.

CHAPTER 13

Shame, Guilt, and Abandonment

Shame:

Genesis 2:25: "Adam and his wife were both naked, and they felt no shame."

Genesis 3:10: Adam said to God: "I heard You in the garden, and I was afraid because I was naked; so, I hid."

It is well-known that in the Bible, God placed a curse on Adam and Eve.

Fear, shame, and guilt go a long way back. It's hard to break tradition, especially since we all fear abandonment as children, and many families then add God into the mixture.

The author John Bradshaw wrote a book on this very subject: *Healing the Shame that Binds You,* and in it he stated that "families are as sick as their secrets." This toxic shame he's talking about is when people in the family refuse to talk about issues such as abortions, addiction, alcoholism, incest, abuse, sexual addictions, or verbal abuse. These all show up in our lives as toxic behaviors. When the body reacts to trauma, the brain gets rewired, becoming hyper-vigilant to anything that may represent that trauma in the future. These unresolved behaviors will manifest as diseases.

Cancer is one of the deepest forms of unresolved toxic shame, guilt, or abandonment.

Adoptees who've never found their parents can suffer from cancers of the blood (blood relative issue). They can also suffer from kidney stones (fear, essence of parents). Kidney stones are also the only thing when we say, "The pain is like giving birth." This pain may take an adoptee back to his or her birth and reactivate the trauma of being abandoned. Adoptees may also suffer from back or spine issues (fear of being unsupported). If adoptees have children, they do their best to fit in -- for fear of their children abandoning them, because the children are their only known blood relatives. They may stay in unhealthy relationships just to keep the peace, even though that may make them very sick. PTSD creates a false narrative based on fear, shame, and guilt; the more years spent in that state, the more the person becomes ill.

A shame-based person will feel flawed at their deepest core and so will seek anything that might alter their mood. They believe that if they try to heal, it will be far too painful, so they smother their emotions with whatever makes them feel good. In the case of breast cancer, we are looking at dairy products—the literal nourishment between mother and child. The milk itself is made with ingredients such as sugar to keep us addicted, and tryptophan to keep us sedated. **Milk is Nature's perfect little drug.**

According to breastcancer.org, dated February 4, 2021, "1 in 8 women in the U.S. will be diagnosed with breast cancer." Many of those cases will be estrogen-positive.

Stealing:

If you ever want to know why people steal, just ask what was stolen from them as a child. Stealing is a replay of something that was taken away from a child too soon. It can take many forms, and it can be something as innocent or borrowed or something like grand theft or even murder (loss of life). The theft will be equal to the original trauma from an emotional standpoint. They're stealing to emotionally fill a hole with what was lost even though the item will never fill the emotional pain. These emotional losses of their childhood can occur over various situations, such as the death of a friend or family member, abuse or molestation, adoption, divorce, moving, or even losing the baby status. To a child, a loss is something that is taken, so the child may constantly try to replace what is lost. The child may even believe that they have the right to steal and may not even equate it with wrongdoing. They may even think that they only "borrowed" the item so it will seem justified, and they may say things like, "I was only going to borrow it for a while," or "you weren't using it," or "I didn't think you'd notice that it was gone." If there's a pattern, more than likely, there's a trauma that the person is trying desperately to compensate for.

CHAPTER 14

Patterns of Addiction

Addiction:

Addiction. So how did we get here? When most people think about addiction, they envision the hard-core addict lying on the side of the road, all tweaked out. But without addiction, we wouldn't survive. As soon as we are born, our very first day is about survival and addiction. The body is a complex system of self-regulation for survival; addiction, the cycle of pain and pleasure, helps keeps us alive. The basics of addiction are this: There's a pain that causes our need, or desire, to be satisfied (pleasure). As the pain and discomfort increase, we start to look for the "thing" that will make that go away, which in turn will make us feel normal, or regulated.

Remember all addictions are interchangeable.
You just need a new reward.

Our very first addiction is breast milk. As babies, when we're hungry, our bodies feel pain, and we cry out. This activation causes the mother to feel pain in her breasts. When the baby latches on to her breast, there's relief for both mother and child, physically, emotionally, and hormonally. The nipple and the brain are directly connected, and the mother is affected by the hormones prolactin and oxytocin. Prolactin is most predominant at night, so when the baby is fed at night, the mother will feel calmer and will be able to sleep better. Oxytocin also has a calming effect, and will increase the bond between mother and child. The baby gets that warm contact with the mother, and with two potent ingredients in breast milk -- tryptophan and lactose. The tryptophan acts as a sedative, and the lactose has a similar effect as cocaine on the brain, by affecting the dopamine or feel-good receptors. That's why babies conk out after feeding -- they are literally drugged up and knocked out. So, the benefit of the infant's addiction includes both nourishment and survival.

When babies, or mothers, can't breastfeed, or choose not to, this may start a pattern of physical and emotional pain and a disconnect between mother and child, or even abandonment issues. In addition, when a baby cannot breastfeed, he or she is put on a substitution, most likely dairy-based. Again, this reinforces the dairy addiction and its association with mother.

Many people are allergic or lactose-intolerant to dairy. Symptoms of an autoimmune reaction are gas or bloat, runny nose, congestion in the throat, cough, diarrhea, or constipation. As the person ignores these physical symptoms and unresolved emotions, the symptoms will increase in severity, to allergies, fatigue, menstrual issues, or early menstruation (average age starts at around age 14), excessive breast growth (male and female), or irregularities in bowel movements. I have enjoyed helping new moms with their gassy and bloated babies; when the diet or formula that contains dairy is changed, the baby gets relief.

As the addiction to dairy continues, and the unresolved emotions remain, the physical symptoms increase. This can develop into diseases such as endometriosis, severe allergies or asthma, mental fogginess, Crohn's or irritable bowel, extreme fatigue with dull aches, and eventually life-threatening illnesses such as breast cancer.

Because addiction is based on the pain/pleasure cycle, to break this pattern we must seek happiness. However, happiness is not the same as pleasure. Pleasure is only a temporary fix to a problem, and when the pleasure wears off, the problem or pain is still there. On the other hand, happiness holds greater meaning because we understand the problem and explore the solution, even though the situation may never be solved. Gaining the ability to look at the problem, emotion, or pain from different viewpoints will allow us to break the pain/pleasure-seeking pattern. As a result, we will find more profound understanding and compassion towards the problem, emotion, or pain.

I have often described to my patients that if you grow a disease such as cancer, then in many cases, you can ungrow it. People often spend years nourishing a dysfunctional relationship as if it was a bond made of *love*, which has actually grown and flourished into a disease. Only when we come to our tipping point do we get that "come to Jesus" or "hit the wall" moment so that we can start to heal and nourish ourselves, releasing old, worn-out patterns that no longer serve us.

In order to heal from these broken patterns, one must reflect on the mind, body, and spirit simultaneously. For example, an inflammation such as cancer can only grow in an oxygen-deprived, acid environment, so in order to kill the disease, deprive the cancer of nourishment. In many cases, if you feed an addiction, the outcome is usually death, but if you feed life, love, happiness, and truth, the result will usually be a long, healthy life.

"The meaning of all addictions could be defined as endeavors at controlling our life experiences with the help of external remedies. Unfortunately, all external means of improving our life experiences are double-edged swords: there are always good and bad. No external remedy improves our condition without, at the same time, making it worse."
Thomas Hora, MD, *Beyond the Dream: Awakening to Reality.*

"It's hard to get enough of something that almost works."
-- Vincent Felitti, MD

When we think of an addict, that might be hard-core alcoholics, or drug addicts who are homeless -- people most of us are afraid to look because of our own fear, shame, and guilt. If we choose to look at them, we'll see a human being struggling with their "hurt inner child" issues - raw and exposed to the world. This is scary to our own inner child, because we will see part of our own hurt selves, even though we fail to admit that even exists. Many addicts have been exposed to abuse as children -- sexual abuse, physical or mental abuse, abandonment, rejection, humiliation, character assassination. Having experienced something in their life that has altered their emotional course, they have become addicted, in order to numb out their emotions and feel "normal." This only perpetuates their hurts, both emotionally and physically, repeatedly. Addiction allows protection from emotional pain by helping us cope and gives us what we think is "normalcy." The addict believes that they feel better when "using" or "stuffing," but the reality is completely the opposite. As a result, they become emotionally and physically drained, along with having increasing symptoms of depression, and a feeling of isolation.

It's easy to see the patterns in such extreme cases, but we don't quite see it as addiction when it comes to looking at anything else. In the process, we deny what's truly in front of us. Our very first addiction in life *is breast milk.* We need it to thrive, and our addiction keeps us coming back in order to survive. We simply cannot survive without it in some form. The lactose in breast milk helps the body release endorphins such as dopamine and serotonin, and the "rush" makes the baby feel calm, sedated, nurtured, and protected. It bonds mother and child. Have you ever seen someone try to wean a child off the breast? You'll see the addiction withdrawals, but we never seem to quite call it that.

What about the kid who has an absolute meltdown in the candy aisle? It's because once the baby no longer has access to this feel-good drug called breast milk, they go into a fight, flight, or freezing response (PTSD), and the baby feels separated and unprotected. These are survival instincts at their most primal root. Remember the breast milk? It's like candy, because it contains sugar, which is highly addictive. How many times have you eaten food that you keep going back to because it makes you feel good? Dairy is the ultimate substitute for the original addiction, and that's why it's so powerful; it makes us feel good and smooths out the problems of the day. It sedates us and keeps us addicted, especially if there's an emotion we don't want to feel, such as an unresolved trauma from our childhood. Many of us can't even remember what the trauma was, or if we do as adults, we say it's really no big deal or blow it off, and we fail to process it by exploring our feelings. As children, it's easy to feel good and relaxed when we have a big bowl of ice cream. We feel soothed and calm as the ingredients hit our digestive tract and brain. It seems like whatever stressed us out now magically seems to disappear. As we get older, we start to find similar feel-good foods such as chocolate, ice cream, and cheese.

The addiction to sugars such as lactose in dairy will affect the neurotransmitters in the brain, which temporarily enhances the brain's dopamine function, but when the brain gets flooded with sugar, such as the lactose in dairy, and the brain has to balance itself out by decreasing the dopamine receptors. As a result, the brain starts to build up a tolerance, and now we want more to make ourselves "feel good," which will start to numb the five emotions: pensiveness, grief or sadness, anger, joy, and fear, which are essential to experience so we can recover from our unresolved childhood traumas.

Sugars like lactose in the dairy act on the brain similarly to cocaine, which is similar to Prozac, which regulates mood and serotonin levels.

In the book *In the Realm of the Hungry Ghost* by Gabor Mate, MD., Dr. Richard Rawson, Associate Director at the University of California, Los Angeles, Integrated Substance Abuse Program, stated, **"Food-seeking can increase brain dopamine levels by 50%."** This is the starting point for food to affect the body's pathology, which will eventually affect the body, mind, and spirit. For example, sugars such as lactose in dairy will start to inflame the brain, altering mood and thought processes.

Children need parents or caregivers until about the age of 15, and during this time, we are under parents' influence. As babies, all of our responses are based on what we see, feel, and smell, and our body's nervous system will react to these subtle differences, which can either cause a positive or a negative response, and trigger the brain and body to respond to, "Do I feel safe?" Some of my earliest memories of both my father and brother was that they used to give me "the look" that scared the crap out of me. That fear is still in my subconscious, and has made me wary of males, especially when they give me the "look." When it pops up, I must be conscious of my emotions in order to recognize the trigger and heal from that unwanted behavior.

In the book *The Body Keeps Score,* by Bessel Van Der Kolk, MD, he states, "Almost all mental suffering involves either trouble in creating workable and satisfying relationships, or difficulties in regulating arousal (as in the case of habitually becoming enraged, shut down, overexcited, or disorganized). Usually in a combination of both."

A *loving* social support is the key to a fundamental and healing relationship. If we feel that we are heard, or in someone's thoughts, we can begin to let go and heal from the patterns that no longer serve us. As children, when we feel imminent danger, we'll first turn to family and friends for support; when we don't feel supported, our response system turns to our primal brain response of fight, flight, or freezing. In the words of Pavlov, that damages our "reflex purpose," which is our ability to organize our living space, friends, family, and healing purpose in society. As a result, the trauma is what he called "learned helplessness." This will trigger all our pathological responses in the brain and organ systems, and as a result, the only time we will feel excited and alive is when we feel the trauma. The trauma pattern then becomes our "new normal." People will no longer feel normal in a calm, *loving*, healing relationship, either with themselves or others. As a reaction, they will constantly look for relationships, jobs, stressors, addictions, or foods to keep themselves triggered in order to feel normal and have a sense of purpose.

In response to our survival instinct, we'll mimic the behaviors -- both consciously and subconsciously -- of others to avoid abandonment. During this time of dependence and survival, we adapt these unhealthy patterns from our caregivers, and we start to develop coping skills due to the stress of maintaining our balance. This stress --due to adaptation of our surroundings -- activates the brain's process of addiction, because now it must compensate for this new mood alteration. To do this as kids, we seek out foods to regulate ourselves.

When we look at foods as infants, our first fixation is oral -- to our mother's breast. When that is taken away, we will compensate and find another source to comfort ourselves—this is why dairy is such a strong substitute for our original addiction. By nature's design, it's the perfect nourishing feel-good food. It gives us the same sensation we got when breastfeeding as infants. We feel calm, *loved*, and nourished with tryptophan and lactose (sugar), so we can survive and thrive.

As soon as you see the milk, ice cream, yogurt, or cheese, your desire increases, and your brain releases dopamine, and all those feel-good memories come flooding back at you and your connection with your mother, and you start to feel soothed and comforted -- just as you did as a baby. Dopamine is also responsible for your survival instinct, so your brain feels like, "If I don't have it, I'm going to die."

So your need for dairy products has now become an addiction, and without it, the brain tells you, you may not survive. Dairy helps you soothe the broken bond between mother and child or, in some cases, the relationship between you, the adult, and your child, or lack thereof. Adults will be triggered subconsciously when they have their own children, who are now painful reminders of what you couldn't get from your parents. There may also be hurt feelings when you see your parents and how they treat their grandkids, because it may be completely different than how they raised you. You might start feeling angry or jealous over their newfound *love* and kindness over your kids that you never got to experience. Now, to soothe your hurt feelings, you'll seek out dairy. Anything you see that reminds you of dairy is now a trigger, because dopamine is being released. The opioid system is responsible for pain and pleasure, which flood your brain with all those feel-good hormones. Once the brain is activated, the opioid system is responsible for the reward attachment system. The dopamine receptors are responsible for incentive and motivation, and the prefrontal cortex is responsible for self-regulation.

In some cases, this is why it's so hard for cancer patients to give up dairy. Their brain tells them that they'll lose all those feel-good emotions they had when breast-feeding, and that the mother-child bond will be broken if they stop. No one wants to lose mommy's *love* or be abandoned.

Once this addictive pattern is established, we start to lose control, and parts of the brain will lose their function. In addition, the lactose in the dairy will start to inflame the brain, leading to depression, which may increase the need to feed your addiction to dairy, in order to maintain the "feel-good" sensation. Because of its powerfully uplifting ingredients, dairy also actually gives us the feeling of being *loved*.

CHAPTER 15

How Trauma Forms

"Enter through the narrow gate. For wide is the gate and broad is the road that leads to destruction, and many enter through it." Matthew 7:13

Emotional Unavailability:

From a child's point of view, whoever raises them, they are their everything, but the child may be an issue to the adult. Emotional unavailability is something many parents face, and finding a healthy balance is vital to the child and the parent. Some signs of an emotionally unavailable parent are: when they are away from the child, the child never crosses their minds. This can even happen when they are in the same room. The parent's attention is somewhere else, but not on the child. Some parents only want to entertain the child when it's something fun for them, otherwise they won't stick around to just be bored with the child. The parent may excuse why they can't commit to a time, place, or play with the child. The parent may enjoy spending time doing their own thing vs. spending time with the child. There are times when the parent can send mixed messages or make promises they know they can't keep.

They never seem committed or have concrete plans. As a result, the child may feel resentful or guilty, and may have to compete for the parent's attention. The parent will hate to be questioned by the child over lack of commitment or communication, and the parent will feel pressed or cornered, and so avoid hard or truthful conversations, or may even react negatively to stop or control the conversation. This will allow them to be emotionally off the hook so that they can carry on without expectations. The child may only be part of their life, such as when they are in the house, but the parent won't go to games or functions for the child because of their own emotional needs and wants. The more the child questions them, the more the child's expectations rise, and the parent will counter to make themselves feel better and in control through distance, anger, belittling, shaming, favoritism, ghosting, or redirecting a conversation.

Parentification:

According to *Wikipedia*: "Parentification is the process of role reversal whereby a child is obliged to act as parent to their own parent. In extreme cases, the child is used to fill the void of the alienating parent's emotional life. Two distinct modes of parentification have been identified technically: instrumental parentification and emotional parentification. Instrumental parentification involves the child completing physical tasks for the family, such as looking after a sick relative, paying bills, or providing assistance to younger siblings that a parent would normally provide. Emotional parentification occurs when a child or adolescent must take on the role of a confidant or mediator for (or between) parents or family members."

Where did mommy go?

The mother-child bond is so strong that the child believes that mommy should be focused only on them, thanks to all the hormones, emotions, and mirroring neurons. When mommy has to work, go to school, or, God forbid, date, the limbic system kicks in, and the child goes into fight, flight, or freezing, fearing abandonment.

"Why would she ever leave me?"

The child starts to feel an increase in fear and anxiety, going from a safe environment into the unknown too soon in their life. From the brief time my mother attempted to date, I felt a lot of jealousy and anger, hoping that it would never work out. As a child who was already going through enough imbalance, I would never want my mom to be taken away from me or be distracted by some outsider. Mothers who have their inner child trauma are looking for the daddy or mommy they never had. The inner child longs for a close, safe and nurturing relationship, so mothers can become distracted by their own needs of wanting a close and *loving* relationship. Looking for this fleeting *love* in a relationship can cause additional time away from their children.

Abortion:

According to a study written in the *Journal of American Physicians and Surgeons: Women Who Suffered Emotionally from Abortion: A Qualitative Synthesis of Their Experiences,* by Priscilla K. Coleman, Ph.D.; Kaitlyn Boswell, B.S.; Katrina Etzkorn, B.S.; and Rachel Turnwald, B.S. Results: "Among the 987 respondents, 13% reported having visited a psychiatrist, psychologist, or counselor prior to the first pregnancy, resulting in an abortion, compared to 67.5% who sought such professional services after their first abortion. Only 6.6% of respondents reported using prescription drugs for psychological health prior to the first pregnancy that ended in abortion, compared with 51% who reported prescription drug use after the first abortion. These data suggest that the women as a group were generally psychologically healthy before their first abortion. Concerning potential risk factors for adverse reactions to abortion, 58.3% of the women reported aborting to make others happy, 73.8% disagreed that their decision to abort was entirely free from even subtle pressure from others to abort, 28.4% aborted out of fear of losing their partner if they did not abort, 49.2% reported believing the fetus was a human being at the time of the abortion, 66% said they knew in their hearts that they were making a mistake when they underwent the abortion, 67.5% revealed that the abortion decision was one of the hardest decisions of their lives, and 33.2% felt emotionally connected to the fetus before the abortion."

I have met many women who have said that an abortion was not their idea, and that it was done to keep someone else happy. Women who relied on someone else to make the decision, in many cases did not put forth any input, for fear of rejection or abandonment. Society had chastised abortion, which is an unfair judgment, and women grieve and agonize over these decisions. Some women take many years to heal and resolve these emotions, and some never at all but either way it is gut-wrenching for them. One cannot walk in another's shoes, and it's not for us to judge another human being.

When I was 19 years old, I got pregnant. I have never even been to a gynecologist. I was unmarried,

1,000 miles away from home, in college, with no job or insurance, and it was my boyfriend who decided that I would have an abortion. Many things were going through my head at the time, and one thought was, "I didn't want to be nauseous." I'd left home for this man and thought that *love* meant doing what he told me. I didn't want to be abandoned by him.

Unfortunately, I ended up abandoning myself and my unborn child for what I thought was *love*. It took me about 30 years to let go of the anger, which poisoned myself, and my marriage to the same man, and to grieve the loss of my child. I did my best at the time to rationalize my poor decisions. It's these moments in my life that I knew I had to face in order to grow and heal. Even though it was gut-wrenching at the time, I own the responsibility, so I can help others heal and grow. Life is messy and complicated, and we cannot hold others in judgment, especially when we fail to look at and own our own lives.

Adoption:

> **"Denial is terror, and many regain the reality or bravery too late, that most adoptees fear the truth."**
> **-- Joel Soll--Author**

An article written in the *Huffington Post* called *Adoption-Related Trauma and Moral Injury*, by Mirah Riben, Dec. 6, 2017, states: "For the adoptee, adoption is a trauma of loss and separation that can result in PTSD. Mothers who lose children to adoption also experience a trauma that can cause PTSD, but in addition, they experience 'moral injury.' Adoption wounds. It wounds the souls of the children and their mothers and fathers, who are torn apart in order to form new families. We also know now that trauma passes genetically to future generations." Later in the article, adoptive mother Nancy Newton Verrier describes the trauma of being "separated from the voices, rhythms, and smells of the womb as *The Primal Wound*."

In an online article dated November 6, 2013, by Bryan Post from the *Post Institute* on his blog: "Whether adopted from birth or later in life, all adopted children have experienced some degree of trauma. Trauma is any stressful event which is prolonged, overwhelming, or unpredictable. Though we are familiar with events impacting children such as abuse, neglect, and domestic violence, until recently, the full impact of trauma on adopted children has not been understood. Scientific research now reveals that as early as *the second trimester, the human fetus is capable of auditory processing and in fact, is capable of processing rejection in utero*. In addition to the rejection and abandonment felt by the newborn adoptee, or any age of adoptee, for that matter, it must be recognized that the far greater trauma often occurs in the way in which the mind and body system of the newborn is incapable of processing the loss of the biological figure. Far beyond any cognitive awareness, this experience is stored deep within the cells of the body, routinely leading to states of anxiety and depression for the adopted child later in life."

An adoptee spends their whole life trying to fit into a place where they naturally don't belong. I have had adoptees tell me that they don't look like their siblings, they scan crowds for people who look like them, or if they know their birth name, they will search for people with the same name. Some of them have their birth certificates withheld only to find the papers later hidden or locked up, revealing their birth name. Some will wait until their adoptee parents pass away to start looking for their birth family, for fear of being abandoned.

The Passing of Mom:

In an article on vice.com called *How the Death of a Parent Affects a Child,* By Virgie Townsend: "An estimated 1.5 million U.S. children lose one or both parents by the age of 15." This is a whole level of hurt, and a huge hole that has opened up in these kids. I was lucky because my parents separated when I was two, and my father killed himself when

I was 6, so I had minimal contact or memories of my father. But the reality for me was that it *did* have an impact. I have no memory of conversations; I cannot picture him or hear his voice, nor do I remember ever being hugged by him. See, I never really got to see a husband-and-wife relationship. I knew how to be a mom 'cause I was raised with one, but I never really understood the interactions between a husband and wife. I was never a good wife, but I was an excellent mother, and I even picked someone who wanted and needed a mother, and he ended up being my only child. I even chose someone whose father died when he was a child. **Trauma *loves* trauma.**

For the many children who lose their moms, it's a whole different level of hurt. During your childhood, your mirroring neurons are most active, because they are designed to keep us thriving, and when the parent you're mimicking for survival dies, a subconscious panic starts to occur. Not only is the death traumatic, but now your brain is asking, "How are we going to survive? We may perish." With all of this working in your brain, it's no wonder children have an increase in sleeplessness, anxiety, depression, excessive thoughts about dying, or can become sexually active because they are longing for that intimate relationship they lost. The whole family has to adjust to this new normal, and each person grieves differently. As the roles and dynamics change, the child may have to take up a more grownup role, which is something they are not used to, such as cooking, cleaning, being responsible for a sibling (parentification). There is also an economic impact that may cause the family to change their lifestyle, which can be drastic.

A woman whom I met on my trip to California shared her story with me that she was a toddler when her mother died giving birth to her sister. As a result, she struggles with stress and anxiety, and her sister died from breast cancer. Though children maybe be very young, when these traumas happen, the body and mind will remember this sudden shift, leading to PTSD.

Happy Birthday:

Birthdays, the most important day of the mother-child bond. There has been no research regarding PTSD in infants swept away from their mother for health reasons after birth, but no one has to look very far to see that trauma, as it is well documented in adoptees and birth moms. This information will give you a glimpse into how traumatic it can be when a child is taken away from its mother. As we say in medicine, "seconds count," which is also true in the mother-child bond. Imagine what it's like for a baby who has lived its whole life in a safe, warm, nourishing, and comfortable environment for about ten months, and the only home you've known suddenly disappears. All gone within seconds. The separation activates the limbic system into fight, flight, or freezing mode; the child will cry for its mother and starts to shake uncontrollably as a result of this activation. In some cases, when the child has been separated and then reintroduced to their mother, they will not attach or bond right away and can appear disconnected and detached, no longer trusting the mother because of abandonment and the activation of the limbic system. These kids may have attachment or bonding issues in the future.

Moms and the NICU:

Many studies have researched PTSD of mothers with infants in the NICU, and there can be as much as a 50% increase in postpartum depression and PTSD, especially in first-time mothers. Some mothers experience increased symptoms such as intrusion, obsession, distressing thoughts, upsetting flashbacks, body symptoms, flashbacks, dreams or nightmares or arousal, anxiety, irritability, panic attacks, on-guard, anger outburst, easily startled, sleep issues. Along with this, the mother could be wracked with guilt or shame and feel that they've done something wrong or think that somehow, they deserved it, thinking that they're a bad mother. They're not! These feelings can happen with any mother, especially when the child is disabled or what society thinks is less than perfect. Each child is beautiful and special, and they all have their unique gifts. They are the angels that have come down from the heavens to teach us unconditional love, and each day with them is a gift.

Handicapable:

I have the privilege of helping women with their infertility issues, and I can tell you that no one thinks about having less than a perfect and healthy child. Ten fingers, ten toes. But nature has her own plans, and to her, **all children are perfect**. I've watched firsthand my own mother's struggles with my brother David, who is high-functioning Autistic. She carried so much guilt and shame, especially after he was in a state mental institution, and would call her, asking to come home. This wracked her with emotions, and she would say, "I wish he wouldn't call, or I wish he would just die." I knew she never meant it, because she was a very *loving* mother, but it was all she could do to cope with the situation. Why do I know she was a good mom? Because she suffered from manic depression and was in and out of the mental hospital when I was a kid.

Looking back, the rest of us needed her at home, but her illness was as deep as the *love* she had for all of us. If she hadn't struggled, I think I would've been worried.... The struggle is real, and it doesn't go away. There is a financial and emotional struggle, as well as being an outcast in society. But I wouldn't have it any other way. My big brother is a brilliant, sensitive, and intuitive man, and I'm thankful every day for him. Handicapable people develop superpowers and are not like us average human beings. They are uniquely gifted, to make up for the ordinary.

Sexual Abuse:

It is a horrible thing to talk about, and the reality for many is that it's happening all too frequently, especially since sex trafficking is making the news more often. These news reports will trigger victims who have not had the opportunity to heal from their own traumatic experiences fully. For some, this is a deep-rooted issue, and it's a topic that many avoid or stuff. One of the issues with PTSD is denial, which causes a person not even to remember that anything ever happened. Still, the illnesses, disease, and emotional factors are there for everyone but the victim to see. I have worked with people with weight issues who wanted hypnosis to lose weight, and during the session, it's discovered that they were sexually abused. They have been using weight to protect themselves. This form of trauma is exasperated when the child tries to tell their parent or guardian and is dismissed, betrayed, or devalued by the person who should have protected them. Some children will imagine that they are "bad," and that they deserved the abuse. This is the only form of what they think is *"love* and attention," and the child fears rejection, betrayal, and a loss of self-esteem.

I met a person who was in a relationship with a married man; she said she and her partner liked to role-play during sex. She always played the part of "mommy" for her partner. I asked if her partner, was ever sexually abused, and she said, "Yes, by his mother." Sometimes a person will go back to the scene of the crime as an unhealthy way to rekindle the broken bond.

I remember a time with my neighbor, who was at the age of first exploring sex, and I am thankful that he didn't know enough to do some repeated damage. He did touch my private parts to his private parts, but that was it. I grew up in a rural area, and my godmother had a farm with goats, and I knew enough that when goats "touched," they had babies. So, when I got home, I asked my mom, "Can I get pregnant?" She said, "No, you're too young." And nothing more was said. But as that little girl, I was worried about how I was going to tell my mom I was pregnant. Innocent enough, but an everlasting memory.

There are many patients I've met who have gone through some horrible situations, and I am here to tell you that: **You are not alone; you are part of a majority;** and it's so important to share your stories, however small, disgusting, humiliating or anguished... It's part of your healing journey, and will help you, and others, heal.

I have seen some very unhealthy people carry these burdens for so many years; it's time to let these secrets out. Allow your forgiveness to come out, because the more you hold on, you'll start to rot from the inside. There are many safe ways to approach your healing, so find what works and then get it all out. As children, we need our parents' protection, and there are many people who never felt protected by their mothers. In some cases, the mother dismissed the child in favor of the spouse, uncle, aunt, grandparent, siblings, or friend......This is a horrible betrayal to the child and locks the child into that trauma. **I am here to tell you that your voice is valued and heard, and is welcomed, and so is your healing.** Many of us see your screaming inner child who wants to be *loved* and validated, and we are here to listen. But it's up to you to want to release all the burdens you are carrying. If you feel that something is wrong or deep inside you feel disconnected or off or uncomfortable, reach out for help and guidance. There will always be a healthy way for you to heal.

Don't give up on yourself!

Birth Moms and Adoptees:

While there are many successful adoption cases, some have breast cancer who are either a birth mom or an adoptee. Keep in mind that all of these women and their children suffer from PTSD. Having a child is the most natural thing for women. It's what we're built for. All mothers have their child's DNA floating in their bloodstream for the rest of their lives. Think about it. That connection never goes away, and we can never be separated from it. As a natural response in many cases, the memories of this trauma get blocked out emotionally and stuffed, so they can try and go on with their new, altered life. I have talked to many women who have suffered breast cancer and shared their stories of what happened as a birth mother. Unfortunately, birth moms are usually not the only decision-maker when it comes to giving up their children.

In some cases, it can be the parents, grandparents, or partner who suggest that giving up a child would be the best decision, but a superficial decision such as giving up a child can have some profound emotional consequences. Some websites talk about adoption and speak about deep emotional trauma—such as Joe Soll's website adoptionhealing.com. In addition, books like Nancy Verrier's *The Primal Wound* and Ann Fessler's *The Girls Who Went Away,* talk about the deep shame and humiliation that these birth mothers feel and the wounds of an adopted child.

I have seen birth moms who felt like they were dying inside, only to go to the doctor to find out there is nothing wrong. Some of them have never even told anyone that they were mothers, or birth mothers who have completely disconnected from their parents, who decided to give up their grandchild. Many of these women are riddled with anger and grief, and every Mother's Day, birthday, or holiday or perhaps seeing a mother and child together can be a daily reminder of what they have lost. Many people from the outside never even recognize that these women have PTSD due to giving up their children. Many of these women will cling to the nourishment of mother and child, which will be any form of milk product, such as ice cream, yogurt, milk chocolate, cheese, or milk, all with the intent of nourishing that broken relationship.

Adoptees:

From the moment the child is separated from their mother, they go into fight, flight, or freezing, and they scream and cry for their mothers; this trauma alters their DNA. There have been adoptee moms who say that when their adopted child is crying in their arms, they will cry, "I want my mommy," only to be inconsolable. Imagine what it would be like to pretend to fit into another family that is not your own, or constantly scanning crowds for someone who looks like you. Imagine longing every holiday that someday your mom will suddenly appear to take you home. Adoptees are some of the best actors in the world, and all should be Academy Award winners.

Gays and Lesbians:

As a child, the fear or thought about losing your parent's *love* or being abandoned by them is a horrible situation. Childhood is a time where we need our parents, and our mirroring neurons are most active. Our instincts are strong to "fit in" in order to survive, primarily until the age of 15. Having heterosexual parents when you're not heterosexual will be an inner struggle for the child trying to mirror their parents in order to survive. More people are coming out at an early age, and it's nice to see parents being supportive, but there are still many people who have not come out. Many are frozen in fear and leading lives that are a betrayal to themselves. Since they are hurting in the process, everyone around them will subconsciously feel that something is off. We all hope that our parents will *love* us unconditionally, but when they suffer from their trauma, they will act it out on someone else, so there is no guarantee how they will react. I have seen young children confident in themselves who were comfortable in their sexuality, and I have seen adults living a heterosexual lie to fit in, especially in religious families. Many are in the public eye and feel that if they don't play it "straight," they'll lose their jobs or their following. The most important thing is to be true to who you are and be honest, loving, and supportive of yourself. If you feel that you need support or guidance in coming out, please seek out that support. There are many outlets to find the support that best works for you.

Parentification:

There are different forms of parentification, and in all cases, the child is required to "grow up" and assume some type of parental responsibility. For example, the child may be responsible for taking care of a sick parent, or even a sibling, and may feel personally responsible for their well-being. This burden can make them think that if they don't take care of this person, they may die, and, out of fear of abandonment, they take on this emotional and physical burden. The role can include financial support for the parents, and in some cases, the child can assume all or part of the financial responsibility for their parents and the household.

Other forms of parentification can occur when older siblings take on the responsibility of their younger family members, such as waking them up, dressing them, getting them off to school, cooking for them, and any other daily tasks that a parent usually does.

When children are younger, one of their greatest fears can be abandonment, which can lead a child into parentification to hold the family together. I have met women who suffer from anxiety because they feel personally responsible for their siblings' health and well-being. Yet, some of them continue to "parent" their siblings well into their 50s and beyond.

The parent may use their child as a confidant to talk about addiction issues, relationship problems, or childhood traumas. When these situations happen, the child will lose a parent that they can talk to and confide in, and will start to feel the burden of responsibility for taking care of their parent. As the child becomes an adult, they may seek a partner dependent on them in order to re-live the burden of their childhood, which can lead to resentment and disappointment in their partner, all the while never knowing that the pattern is the result of their role of "parent" as a child.

In an article dated March 23, 2017, in the *Washington Post,* called, *Your Child is Not Your Confidant* by Cynthia Lamothe, she talks about research done by Lisa M. Hooper. "When a child starts serving as a friend to the parent, and the parent is getting his or her needs met through the child – that becomes problematic." Her research has shown that the effects of childhood parentification can be long-lasting and multigenerational.

In one study published in the *Journal of Family Therapy,* dated November 30, 2011 -- *Parentification, and Mental Health Symptoms: Mediator Effects of Perceived Unfairness and Differentiation of Self,* by Peter J. Jankowski, Lisa M. Hooper, Steven J. Sandage , and Natalie J. Hannah, data was collected to evaluate the link between childhood roles and responsibilities and adult psychological functioning. The researchers found that people who experienced early parentification were at an increased risk for anxiety, depression, eating disorders, or substance abuse as adults.

"It's not only children who grow. Parents do too. As much as we watch to see what our children do with their lives, they are watching us to see what we do with ours. I can't tell my children to reach for the sun. All I can do is reach for it myself."
-- Joyce Maynard--Author

CHAPTER 16.

Self-Responsibility

"It takes courage to grow up and become who you really are."
e.e. cummings-- Author

"If the doors of perception were cleansed, everything would appear to man as it is, infinite. For man has closed himself up, till he sees all things thro' narrow chinks of his cavern." ***The Marriage of Heaven and Hell***
William Blake--Author

"Do not conform to the pattern of this world, but be transformed by renewing your mind."
Romans 12:2

The Lie:

In each of these cases, there's a deep wound or trauma that forever alters the course of their lives. As it alters their mind, it also alters their physical body. Stuffing emotions, either consciously or subconsciously, leaves a path of destruction. Children start to suffer and display reactionary behaviors, food cravings, nightmares, headaches, tummy aches, rocking or bouncing, destructive or violent behavior. As parents try to pacify or silence them, they start to feed them whatever they want in order to deal with the unwanted behavior. This only reinforces the trauma and the addiction. Unbeknownst to the parents, they are not in tune with their behaviors and so struggle with their children's unresolved traumas.

Self-Responsibility:

A personal sense of self-responsibility. What do I mean by that? We are all responsible to some degree, but how does that affect our health? It's easy to see others' lack of self-responsibility, and we spend most of our time telling others what to do, rather than turn our own words towards ourselves... Remember: what we attract and surround ourselves with is our reflection. But what if we get breast cancer? Do we blame others, or perhaps God, for this horrible disease? Or will we choose to see it as a blessing and focus our time on self-reflection? Ever wonder why some people die very quickly, or some recover fully, never to suffer from cancer ever again? Perhaps recovery is about someone becoming self-responsible and seeing their self-abandonment. So many times as humans, we find blame and fault in others, but we refuse to see our role in our own lives. What if we lived knowing that everything in life was *exactly* the way it was supposed to be, and our response to that determines what quality of life we will live.

We've all heard survivor stories from prisoners of war, that the captors could never take their liberty or their will to survive. How do people survive these horrific scenarios? Faith? A sense of purpose? Free will? God? Whatever you want to call it, everything comes down to self-responsibility. That moment in your life when you finally have your "come to Jesus" meeting, when you just stop fooling yourself, and there is no one else to blame but you, that person staring right back at you in the mirror. The bad grades, lousy sleeping partners, bad spouses, bad jobs, bad food choices, and destructive health issues are all yours. How you choose to see it, or, in many people's cases, *not* see it, is your free will, and you're completely in charge. I have seen it repeatedly with patients, friends, and family members who cannot get over what they have so deeply buried. So fearful of facing it or bringing it up that it controls their lives and makes them sick. If we have the power to eat right and recover our health, then we have the equal power to make ourselves sick. How we view life is how we live it.

If you tell everyone that you want to live, and then go home and eat a gallon of ice cream, what do you think will happen? Yep, you're going to get sick. The only thing in life you can go by is someone's actions. Words are meaningless without actions. So always pay attention to people's actions, especially your own. Remember, everyone has their own path, and it has nothing to do with yours. It's based on their own past experiences, never on the present or the future.

Child's Mind

> **"I know what I really want for Christmas, I want my childhood back. Nobody is going to give me that.... I know it doesn't make sense, but since when is Christmas about sense, anyway? It is about a child of long ago and far away, and it is about the child of now. In you and me. Waiting behind the door of our hearts for something wonderful to happen," -- Robert Fulgnum. --Author --*All I Really Need to Know I Learned in Kindergarten.***
>
> **"The person...in the grip of an old distress says things that are not pertinent, do things that don't work, fails to cope with the situation, and endures terrible feelings that have nothing to do with the present." Harvey Jackins—Founder of Re-evaluation Counseling**

CHAPTER 17

Breast Cancer Stories:

> **"When an inner situation is not made conscious, it appears outside of you as fate."**
> **Carl Jung--Psychiatrist**

The stories listed below give you an idea of some of the possible emotional causes of breast cancer. Hopefully, these stories will shed some light on the strain between mother and child. These causes can be instantaneous or happen over time. So please keep an open mind. The other issue that I could not cover in these stories is what foods the child was craving. A few of these biographies did talk about dairy consumption, such as ice cream, milk, or cheese as comfort foods, but most authors do not cover these subjects in their books.

The other factor I want you to consider is that none of these stories change the *love* between mother and child.

I've had many breast cancer patients tell me that their relationship with their mother was wonderful, and that's an expected reaction from an adult; but when we are children, we need *love* and protection, from a child's perspective. What seems harmless to an adult can be terrifying or upsetting to a child, so keep an open child-like mind.

The breasts are located in the heart center. Therefore, all breast cancer patients struggle with a disconnection from love or a lack of joy. This can lead to grief and sadness and a sense of loss for these children when the traumas occurred. This can reinforce the possibility of feeling shame, guilt, abandonment, repression, disappointment, helplessness, or embarrassment.

"One of the pitfalls of childhood is that one doesn't have to understand something to feel it. By the time the mind is able to comprehend what has happened, the wounds of the heart are already too deep. The words with which a child's heart is poisoned, whether through malice or through ignorance, remain branded in his memory, and sooner or later they burn his soul."
Carlos Ruiz Zafón -- Author
-- *The Shadow of the Wind*

Angelina Jolie:

In the book *Angelina*, by Andrew Morton, the author talks about Angelina's early years as a child, when her parents separated, and she was raised by her father. Her parents separated after her father Jon started an affair with a young college student, which ended their marriage. Her mother had no clue the affair was going on until Jon, in all his honesty, confessed. As a result, his wife went into a downward tailspin, and froze Jon out of her life. Jon took an apartment in the same building as his wife and kids so he could see them, until one day Angelina's crib showed up at his apartment door. During this time, there was a string of babysitters who raised her, and when someone asked Angie's mother to go and visit her because she needed more time and attention, her mother said, "Angie reminds me so much of Jon right now that I cannot be around her. It's just too painful." So her mother turned her focus to her acting and modeling career, and focused her attention on Angelina's brother, the "chosen" child. Angelina stated, "I've just been staring out the window all my life...thinking there was somewhere I could finally be grounded and happy."

This is an example of the broken mother-child bond through emotional and physical abandonment. She talked about feeling grounded, which would correlate to the Root Chakra (survival) and the spleen (earth element) and the emotion pensiveness/ deep thought or not wanting to think in Traditional Chinese Medicine, which correlate to a secure foundation or childhood. The imbalance in the Root Chakra can indicate sex addiction or dysfunction, poor boundaries, fear, shame, guilt or numbness. This can help explain why she had preventative surgery for the BRCA gene, from an emotional standpoint. When a woman undergoes a mastectomy, she is physically cutting off the nourishment from mother to child. Removing the ovaries and the fallopian tubes is essential for the child's development within the mother, also correlated to the mother-child bond. These surgeries can represent physical as well as unresolved emotional issues.

Judy Blume:

According to *Wikipedia,* one of the catalysts for Blume writing books for young adults was that her parents were not honest about the taboo subject of sex education when she was growing up. When she was about 13 years old, her town experienced three airplane accidents in which 118 people died. Her father, who was a dentist, had the task of helping to identify the dead with dental records. Judy had buried these experiences and emotions for many years until she wrote the book, *In the Unlikely Event*. She has been married three times. She described her first marriage as "suffocating" and her second marriage as "a total disaster." These words that she used to describe her failed marriages could also describe the plane crashes. Her third husband was recently diagnosed with pancreatic cancer which is related to the emotion pensiveness. In addition to breast cancer, she had also been diagnosed with cervical cancer and underwent a hysterectomy.

In Traditional Chinese Medicine, the cervix is associated with the kidney and fear. The cervix is located in the Sacral Chakra, which can include sex issues, feelings of fear or relationships, creativity and fantasy, shame and guilt. When the Sacral Charka is out of balance, it will cause a lack of intimate relationships with both parents and spouses. The deaths from the plane crashes would indicate the inner connection to the kidney in Traditional Chinese Medicine. The kidney is also related to sex or sexuality. This would also explain the topics that she chose to write about for teenagers. In her process of healing and understanding, she decided on the very subject that she felt was essential to understand as a child.

Dorothy Hamill:

Dorothy talks about her upbringing in her book *A Skating Life, My Story*, where both of her parents' families had a history of "unspoken depression." Her parents would partake in nightly cocktails, which was quite common for the generation that went through WWII. Even my parents had evening cocktails. What was unbeknownst to outsiders, and with a family history of depression, the nightly cocktails would increase the symptoms of depression and emotional outbursts. Dorothy stated, "Sometimes it would get ugly. Their screaming at each other would awaken my brother, my sister, and me. Then they would scream at us. Since we knew no difference, we thought this was normal." The question of the day for her and her siblings was, "What kind of mood was Mom in?" Because the alcohol would change her mood, and she would "fly off the handle." Dorothy would "hate" to come home from school and felt that her mother was "mad at her." With the uncertainty of the mood at home, it was natural for her to dedicate more time towards skating, and by the time she was 8, she was skating every day. The following year she spent the summer away from home, training at Lake Placid. She was only allowed to stay because her parents arranged for her to stay at her coach's house. What Dorothy had come to realize was that her coach and his wife, like her parents, enjoyed the mood-altering cocktail hour, which put her back into that stressful home life situation she was trying to avoid.

It's pretty common for children of alcoholic parents to be so stressed out that they consume large amounts of candy or sweets, which Dorothy used to do. This is what I like to refer to as a "dry alcoholic," because if you have ever been to an AA meeting, they serve sodas and cookies. In Traditional Chinese Medicine, the liver is associated with the emotion anger/frustration, which converts the alcohol into sugar, trying to relax the stressed-out liver. In many people, anger/frustration freely comes out when people drink, because these unresolved traumas have been suppressed over time. The saying "I'm so angry I can't see straight" can be associated with the liver, which is responsible for vision in Traditional Chinese Medicine. This is why vision gets impaired when people drink. She mentioned her addiction to candy and sweets, and attention deficit disorder (ADD), which she struggled with in school. This is commonly seen, because many people have a negative side effect to simple sugars such as candy, sweets, sodas. These cause the sugars to spike in the blood, causing inflammation in the brain, which scatters thinking and attention. People diagnosed with ADHD have a genetic component inherited from their families who have an alcoholic background. Whole grains cooked with sea salt and foods that contain fiber, such as whole fruits, will slow the release of sugars, lowering the risk of an inflammatory response. Sea salt and seaweed in the diet will re-mineralize the brain, blood, and bone, increasing focus and awareness. Therefore, people with under-active thyroids have "brain fog" -- there are no essential minerals in the diet to help tonify the thyroid.

Janice Dickenson:

In her book *No Lifeguard on Duty*, Janice Dickenson talks about her early childhood and her two sisters. When Janice was 18 months old, her parents moved to Florida. Her mother was a nurse who suffered an injury that made her dependent on prescription medication. Janice described her relationship with her mother: "I hated my mother...Hated her because she was numbed into oblivion with the pills she'd been prescribed for an old back injury." She described her mother's state as "unseeing" and "unaware." Her father got kicked out of the Navy for fighting, and became a Merchant Marine. While her mother was at work, her father started sexually abusing Janice's older sister. He also tried on occasion to sexually abuse Janice, but instead, she was the one whom he beat. She remembered, "He balled up his big, freckled fist when he came after me." She spent her childhood walking on eggshells, just trying to survive.

In public, the family gave the appearance of a healthy, loving family, but nothing could be further from the truth. She learned how to "compartmentalize." Around her senior year, her father tried again to sexually abuse her; he lost control and attacked her. Luckily, her mother had arrived home from work just in time to stop the fight. This was the first time her mother finally sobered up to the fact that "something" bad was happening. She took Janice to the hospital where she worked, and made the excuse that Janice "fell" to the doctor. When they were alone in the hospital, her mother said, "I know I haven't been much of a mother." Janice has suffered from breast cancer and addiction issues in later years.

Without protection or validation from a parent, anger, frustration, and resentment build up in a child. These emotions, especially towards a mother, would explain why some women opt for breast implants. Since the breast is the nourishment between mother and child, and since they never felt "nourished" as a child, the hurt inner child will seek an alternative by altering the breast, instead of dealing with the deeper emotions. Full breasts give the appearance of "nourishment," and they will fill an empty emotional gap for a time. But if the woman fails to see the emotional loss she sustained as a child, it will only increase the disconnection between the mind and the body. Many women alter their breasts to attract a mate. But they can also attract someone who has their own mother-child bond issues. I think this might also be the reason why so many women get the implants removed -- because they no longer need that false sense of nourishment. Addiction issues can also be carried from one generation to another as a form of *love*. Remember those mirroring neurons that kept us bonded to our parents? Well, they would also play a role in our own addictions as adults. Perhaps her addiction was the bond between her and her mother. *Love* equals addiction.

Queen Mother Elizabeth I

According to *Wikipedia,* on April 21, 1926, the Queen Mother gave birth to Princess Elizabeth II. In the following year, February 1927, Elizabeth I and her husband Bertie set sail for Australia and New Zealand, and by the time she got back to her infant daughter, there had been a six-month separation. All she wanted to do is be with her daughter, and in her own words, she was "miserable at leaving the baby" and constantly fretted over the baby being back in Britain. During the trip, the ship had caught fire, and they had to prepare to abandon the ship, but the crew managed to put out the fire. She had also had suffered from a cold, which kept her from some of her engagements.

In the book *Queen Elizabeth Queen Mother Chronicle of a Remarkable Life, 1900-2000,* after the birth of Princess Margaret in August 1930, they were in "need of a nanny so that they could carry out their royal duties." In July of 1931, Elizabeth I and Bertie were off on a tour to Paris and North America without their daughters. In January 1936, King George V had died, which increased Bertie and Elizabeth I's royal duties. They did their best to balance their duties and family life, and by the time Elizabeth II was ten, she too started to be introduced to her royal duties. However, everything they did was overshadowed by the crisis surrounding Bertie's older brother Edward, who was to become king. Edward was bored with royal life and had "adopted a cavalier attitude to his duties." In 1937, Edward renounced his throne and, as a result, that threw Bertie and Elizabeth I into the spotlight as King and Queen. With their many royal duties and the war breaking out, which added more stress on Elizabeth I, she and Bertie decided to send the girls to Scotland, while she and her husband stayed in London. During WWII, the King and Queen remained in Buckingham Palace, which was bombed, while the girls were moved for safety reasons to different locations, then finally stayed at Windsor Castle.

During this time, the family endured many separations and the stress of her royal duties. Elizabeth I had colon cancer, and according to Traditional Chinese Medicine, the colon is related to the emotion grief/sadness. Breast cancer is connected to the nourishment between mother and child, and the emotions of pensiveness and anger. It is mentioned that Elizabeth I still haunts Windsor Castle. Perhaps she never left her daughters whom she worried over so much.

Nancy Regan:

In her book, *My Turn: The Memoirs of Nancy Regan*, her mother married into a family who'd lost their money during the Depression. By the time Nancy was born, her parents' relationship was in serious trouble. As a result, her father didn't attend her birth. Her mother told her that she was due on the 4th of July, but the "Yankees were playing a doubleheader" ....so "she delayed her birth until July 6." When she was born, she was delivered with forceps, and her mother was "horrified. The skin on my right temple was broken, and my right eye was still closed." The doctor told her mother, "If it doesn't open in two weeks, your child could be blind in that eye." Before her mother was placed under anesthesia for delivery, she overheard the doctor say, "Let's finish up so I can go out and play a round of golf." Her mother told the doctor that she had heard what he had said and then said, "You rushed through the delivery so you could play golf. If my little girl's eye doesn't open, so help me. God, I'm going to kill you!"

Nancy's mother was an actress and was now divorced, so that meant that where Nancy's mother went, Nancy went too. For the first two years of her life, she was a "backstage baby." Once Nancy was potty-trained, her mother decided it was best to have a "normal childhood," so she took Nancy to her sister's home in Virginia. In her mother's diary, she found an entry that said, "How I missed her-terribly." Nancy said in her book, "No matter how kindly you are treated-and I was treated with great *love*-your mother is your mother, and nobody else can fill that role in your life."

When she was about five years old, Nancy got extremely ill with pneumonia and was angry at her mother for not being there. She said, "If I had a little girl, I'd certainly be there if she was sick." Their separation lasted about six years, and though her aunt was a kind, *loving,* and reserved woman, her mother was not. In stark contrast, she would tell "off-color jokes," was boisterous, and had the language of a sailor. When her mother was working in New York, her aunt would take her to see her mother perform in a play. "In one of the first plays I ever saw, the other characters were so mean to my mother that I burst into tears. I refused to talk to anyone in that cast because I thought they had been so mean to Mother." Her mother had to explain that it was just make-believe. "I always dreaded the end of the visits, when I had to leave mother again." She was "thrilled when her mother came to visit, and miserable when she left." (No wonder she was so attached to her husband Ronnie, who was also an actor.) Even though the situation was explained, she still yearned to be with her mother.

One day her mother told Nancy that she wanted to get married, and then said, "It's up to you.... I won't marry Dr. David unless you think I should." Nancy was happy and settled with her aunt, but above all, she wanted to be with her mother. Nancy was her mother's bridesmaid, and "even then, twinges of jealousy" were felt when she saw her mother with her stepdad. It was the same feeling Nancy experienced when she saw her husband with his children. The reality was that she wanted her mommy all to herself, and her transition to this new life was "neither smooth nor easy. I was jealous of their close relationship." When they were sitting on the couch, "I squeezed in and forced myself between them. For more than 20 years, I called him Dr. Loyal."

With her biological father, she "never had much of a relationship" and said that he "couldn't relate to me as a young child." As she got older, her father had made some remarks about her mother that enraged Nancy, and "he got upset and locked me in the bathroom. I was terrified." After that, there were no more visits, and she began a phobia of being locked in a bathroom. At the age of 14, she allowed her stepfather to adopt her.

Her first serious boyfriend, who was "charming, funny, and bright," ran across a train track and was hit by a train and killed. It was a "tremendous shock."

She and Frank had "skirted around the subject of marriage." His mother gave me his cigarette case as a memento. It was a silver case I had given him the previous Christmas, with his name engraved on it. He had been carrying it when he was killed, and I still have it."

Her relationships with her children and stepchildren were not very smooth; they often butted heads and argued. She used the word "estranged" to describe her relationship with her kids, just like her parents did when she was a child.

Nancy underwent a radical mastectomy, even though her tumor was very small. This cutting off the breast would have represented the cutting off her relationship with her mother emotionally and her children. During an interview about breast cancer, she never answered why she had chosen that particular course of treatment. Still, she had felt an obligation to her duty to be by her husband's side, perhaps out of fear of abandonment.

Marion "Pat" Benedict:

No, you won't recognize Pat's name, because she is not well-known, but her story is important because she was a Navy nurse. She helped Betty Ford in her recovery from drugs and alcohol, and many others recovering from addictions.

In her book, *The Silence of the Pain is Deafening,* she said, "I was born into a very dysfunctional home. I absolutely hated it. As a child, my ill feelings towards my home were so intense that I would scream at the walls...." Many different family members raised Pat, and due to those inconsistencies, she learned to distrust grownups. As a result, this caused her to grow inward and suppress her feelings. Around the age of three, her father left home. She and her sister were alone with her manic-depressive mother, in a home where there were "dysfunctional relationships, poverty, and chaos." She felt "misunderstood and alienated. There was an emptiness, a hole inside of me....an aching feeling of abandonment."

Because of her mother's illness, and probably her childhood trauma, her mother was manipulative and played the helpless victim. Her mother was on several different medications for her depression. She would suffer from headaches and other minor illnesses in which she became dependent on the girls' help to nurture her. (Parentification) Her mother also suffered from "mood swings," and Pat found her mother to be "difficult, but it was my unfulfilled desire to interact with my mother that I found so painful. I cannot recall her ever reaching her arms out to hug or kiss me." There was no "warmth, understanding or a compassionate environment." Pat also carried anger and rage for the father she never knew. "When you hate, it's like hating yourself. The other person cannot feel your hatred. Instead, you are the only one who can feel that ugly emotion."

Her mother would manipulate her and her sister to take care of her through her minor illnesses, required "constant attention," and couldn't face being alone. Pat couldn't abandon her mother, even though she hated and resented her and all of her neediness. She even resented her mother for bringing her into this joyless world of dysfunction. Her mother was so withdrawn, people believed that she was a "grieving widow."

Pat became a people-pleaser out of her own needs for survival. Instinctively, children know that they need some form of "parent" to survive and tending to her mom's medical needs was a way of ensuring her survival. She also struggled with being poor, which resulted in used clothing and hand-me-downs. This added to her insecurities, and she felt that people could see her shortcomings. She was also "harassed and humiliated" at family gatherings. She thought she should have been born a boy because boys had more of an advantage. Her mother was strict, suffered bouts of screaming and gave Pat whippings, which lowered her self-esteem. She felt that her strict upbringing "enhanced my addiction to alcohol." She added, "When a person grows up governed by control and constraint, implemented by corporal punishment, a child becomes accustomed to imposed control and fails to develop self-control." Then the child indulges in "negative emotions as a familiar means towards self-control." As a result, the person becomes "dependent on negative emotions to function." This is a classic pattern of addiction, which involves pain and pleasure instead of discovering what truly makes someone happy.

"The divorce of my parents was buried in my mind, crippling me with pain for many years...It has taken me years to learn that I owe respect to my inner thoughts and feelings.... I was a people-pleaser, putting my needs second to the wants around me. Alcohol allowed me to abandon my needs and replace it with self-interest and self-abuse...There are two kinds of love; human and divine are different. They pull us in opposite directions. Sometimes we think that, when we experience human *love*, we are experiencing divine love. However, the human and divine aspects of love are distinctly different. I have often found myself divided between the selfish desire to be physically *loved*, and the need for divine love."

She replaced one form of PTSD with another by becoming a nurse in the Navy, thus repeating the pattern of caretaker for the wounded, whether emotionally or physically. After her retirement from the Navy, she worked at the Betty Ford Clinic helping others overcome their addictions. She, too, suffered from breast cancer.

Betty Ford:

According to *Wikipedia*: Betty started working as a model and dance teacher at the age of 11 to help support her family during the Depression. When she was 16, her father died from carbon monoxide poisoning. When she turned 18, she wanted to leave Michigan and go to New York to study dance, which her mother would not approve of. Instead, she spent the summers in Vermont studying dance; her mother wanted her to stay in Michigan instead of pursuing a dance career in New York.

In her book, *Betty: A Glad Awakening,* by Betty Ford with Chris Chase, she talked about her mother and how she thought she was perfect; and how, during the Depression, her mother was the only income provider for the family. When she was young, she never realized that her father was an alcoholic until after he died. She idolized her mother and wanted to meet her expectations, which was an unobtainable task. When Betty was dancing, she realized that she would never be a great dancer. Her confidence she describes as a child was "shaky;" she believed that people didn't accept her for herself, and as a result, became self-conscious and put herself down. She always tried to measure up to her mother's idea of "perfectionism," and idolized her mother's natural ability to shoulder responsibilities, which Betty couldn't do. I "couldn't shoulder my own problems. I lost respect for myself. No matter how hard I tried, I couldn't measure up to my own expectations." Her expectations led to her drinking to help relieve her feelings of "inadequacy" and to fill up her feelings of "emptiness."

As a teenager, her mother would put Betty to bed "with a cup of tea fortified with whiskey to help relieve a cold or cramps," Betty said about alcohol, "Maybe that first drink was the important one. Maybe it was as an adolescent that I first realized what pleasure and escape a drink could bring." When she was around 12, she drank at a girlfriend's house, and her parents always had a 5 o'clock cocktail. When she went to college, she felt peer pressure to drink and wanted to "fit in," This was when she experienced her first "kinda blackout." When she started dating, she wrote about one of the boys, "He was a very sober fellow," and then stated, "sober didn't appeal to me."

She talked about an old folk song by Rudy Vallee, *The Drunkard Song.*

"There's a tavern in the town, and there my true love sits him down,

And drinks his wine with laughter and with glee, and never, never thinks of me?"

"That was the story of my life with Bill Warren," who was her first husband, and it's where her drinking became an acceptable habit. Her brother Bob was an alcoholic, and after she got divorced, she stopped drinking, and her brother became sober. When she met Jerry (Gerald Ford), he barely drank. He was the all-American hero type that she could now idolize, and she fell right back into the cycle of "perfection" that was created through her vision of her mother. When Jerry started his career in politics and then later became President, she felt abandoned, and less and less important. She had become a "doormat" for her kids. "Self-pity overwhelmed me." She encouraged her husband to drink, but *she* was the one actually drinking, to cope with the pressures of at least looking like the perfect wife, mother, hostess, and First Lady. She would set herself up for a downward spiral of drinking at parties and functions, then later drink alone, yet never thought she was losing control. When she got a pinched nerve in her neck, doctors started to supply her with drugs to cope with the pain. She could hear her mother's voice in her head, "If you can't do it right, don't do it at all."

Betty said, "It took me a long time to quit being a juvenile, acting immature in my recovery. Feelings of inadequacy...An alcoholic can appear to be very conceited, full of braggadocio, but that is all a front, when they are really only struggling with self-pity, anger, and resentment."

"People with low self-esteem always crave reassurance from the outside world."
-- Betty Ford

In her book, there's a quote from her friend Mari Bell Sharbutt: "I lost my way a long time ago. We lose our way by not maturing. We have a lot of fun and a lot of pleasure, a lot of pain getting sober, and a lot of shame. We have a lot of mental attitudes to change. We have the physical recovery. And then we begin to recover the laughter and the joy and the pleasure of not having to pretend any more. And then we begin to find our souls."

Bill Wilson, the co-founder of AA, said of a group that he attended before establishing AA, "I admired the Four Absolutes--absolute honesty, purity, unselfishness, and love."

Betty suffered from alcohol and prescription drug addiction, which in Traditional Chinese Medicine are all metabolized in the liver. The liver is connected to the emotions of anger/frustration. Arthritis is a bone issue related to the kidney, and the emotion fear, and the essence we inherit from our parents. Breast cancer was Betty Ford's connection to both her mother and her children.

Shirley Temple Black:

According to *Wikipedia*: When she was three years old, her mother encouraged her to pursue singing, acting, and dancing; Shirley had a signed contract when she was around four years old, during the Great Depression. Her mother was styling her hair, and her father oversaw her finances; when she was five years old, she was making about $150 per week, had to wear false teeth to hide her baby teeth. Kids would pull her hair, and the public questioned if she was even a child.

In a book by Jean F. Blashfield, *Shirley Temple Black: Actor and Diplomat,* since she was the baby of the family and the only girl, her mother had devoted a lot of time to her. While her mother listened to music and cleaned, little Shirley would make up dance steps and follow her around the house. Her parents decided when Shirley was 3 1/2 that she was going to dance school to learn the steps "correctly," and "it was always important for her to please the adults in her life," especially since her brother suffered from various illnesses.

Hollywood talent scouts visited her dance school, and during a visit, Shirley walked over and said "hello." Her mother "heard nothing from the visit, and Shirley knew her mother was disappointed." The next time the scouts came to visit, Shirley was so frightened that she would disappoint her mother again, she "hid under the piano," but a scout saw her and called her over. This was the beginning of her career; her mother took care of every aspect of it. Shirley got released at the end of her contract, and Shirley's father asked his wife to give up the prospects of an acting career for Shirley, but she refused. After her parents took her to see a movie, Shirley started dancing outside the theater. When someone in the film industry happened to see her, Shirley's career took off. Her mother, whom some would call a "pushy stage mother," oversaw all aspects of Shirley's career -- from helping her with her lines, to learning songs and dances, making her costumes, and hairstyling – "exactly 56 pin curls every night." She also made sure Shirley was well-fed and rested. In return, her mother "was the only person Shirley would listen to," not even the director.

When she was playing in-between takes and the director couldn't find her, he would put her in "time out," which meant an "icy black box." People in the film industry didn't want her to pick up behaviors from other children, so they chose to isolate her from the others and wouldn't allow anyone outside the family, even directors, to compliment her. Her films saved Fox Studio from bankruptcy. The studio wanted to use her as long as possible, so they took excellent care of their money-making star. As she got older, Shirley realized that she had a very different life from other children; even in a room full of people, she felt alone. During a family trip, every stop along the way was "milked for publicity."

There was a quote in the book *The Shirley Temple Scrapbook* by Lorraine Burdick. "To each person who was able to get to her after an appearance, the knowledge that they had seen her, heard her, or touched her was an unforgettable experience. But to Shirley Temple, it was eternal hardship." She had become so popular that it wasn't safe for her to be in public. At the ripe old age of 12, she began her private life, and when she was in school, her teacher noticed "She always seemed to be smiling, even when she was relaxed." Shirley didn't realize this until her teacher said it was "weird" and that "she shouldn't smile all the time."

Shirley was very active during WWII, visiting soldiers and wounded vets; during this time, she met her first husband John Agar, at the ripe old age of 15. She feared that he would be sent off to war, so they married when she was 17. His appeal was that he had no interest in becoming an actor, but when people saw this handsome 6'3" man with Shirley Temple, his mind changed. Later, she discovered his love for both women and alcohol. She said that the marriage "just should never have happened." So, after she gave birth to her daughter, and 18 months of marriage, they got divorced. He was very busy acting, but his alcoholism got the best of him. She made a few movies, and officially retired around the age of 21. She did remarry with Charles Black, and she *loved* the fact that her second husband "never saw my movies" because he was not aware of her fame.

During this time, she came of age to receive the money that she had made, which was around 3 million dollars, only to learn that her father had squandered it. After "almost 20 years of work, she had less than $60,000 left." Shirley said, "For reasons some may find inexplicable, I felt neither disappointment nor anger. Perhaps years of ignoring such matters had insulated me from disillusion." She felt that "the money was gone, and her relationship with her father was far more important: Picking over such corpses of the past is like the task of a carrion crow, disheartening and fruitless."

Shirley's brother suffered from MS, which attacks the spinal column and muscle tissue. In Traditional Chinese Medicine, MS would be related to the emotion pensiveness (deep thought) and the fear of being supported (kidney and bone). Shirley was a lifelong smoker, and the lung in TCM is related to the emotions of grief and sadness. All those years she worked to support her family -- only to find out that she was the one who needed the emotional support. Shirley struggled with breast cancer, which would correlate to parentification, financially supporting her parents, and emotional abandonment. She would have felt the pressure of putting income and success before her needs as a child. This stress would also be linked to her fear of disappointing her mother.

Melissa Etheridge:

In her book *The Truth is...My Life in Love and Music* by Melissa Etheridge and Laura Morton, she says that after her experience with a past life regression hypnosis, she experienced trauma and pain during the birth portion of the session. When she asked her mom about her birth, her mom told her that she was "held back for 15 minutes" until the doctors had arrived. As a result of being left in the birth canal too long, she experienced pain and felt a crushing sensation, had black-and-blue marks, as well as a hematoma on her chest (heart chakra/joy and love).

Along with this traumatic birth, she was born on her sister's 4th birthday, which her sister never let her forget. They were forced to have joint birthdays, which increased the strain on their relationship. The sisters were polar opposites. Her sister Jennifer was tall and beautiful, and Melissa was a tomboy. Her sister would constantly torment Melissa and find ways to scare her. As they became older, her sister would want to play "doctor" with her, which led to sexual abuse. Her parents were never emotional people, and as a child, Melissa felt a sense of abandonment and shame. To comfort herself, she turned to food and music. The only person she felt a maternal bond with was her grandmother.

Deeply embedded in our minds is the fear of abandonment. As a child, when your birthday as an individual is not even recognized, this will naturally increase the feeling of unimportance.

After she was diagnosed with breast cancer, she said in an interview with Bryan Buttler on phillymag.com called *INTERVIEW: Melissa Etheridge on Becoming a Gay Icon, Defeating Breast Cancer, and Why You Should Bring an Extra T-Shirt to Her Concert* "It completely changed me. It made me stop and really look at my health and my happiness. If I don't have those two, I'm not good for anything. My health is my number one priority. There's no excuse; in fact, that word is not even in my lexicon." This shift allowed her to re-think her nutrition, --what she's eating, and if she's treating her body well. To use her words, "food is medicine. We've got to get that into our heads."

Trauma involving our mothers can start early in the womb, and the baby being "held back" would cause both mother and child to feel stress. The body will hold onto this trauma, which can affect us subconsciously until it is recognized and then released.

Olivia Newton-John:

In *Olivia: The Biography of Olivia Newton-John*, by Tim Ewbank, she states, "My parents' divorce made me feel insecure. I tried to blank out what was going on. I was always the happy child trying to keep everyone else happy." Olivia was born in England. Her father had ambitions to become an opera singer, but because he thought his musical talents were not good enough, he went into college teaching instead. When Olivia was a toddler, she found some medicine on a table and took it, becoming seriously ill, and "was rushed to the hospital to have her stomach pumped." At the age of five, her parents decided to move to Australia for her father's work. On the boat trip, she recalled having "sadness and tears at somehow losing her favorite soft toy animal comforter, called Fluffy, somewhere along the way." As a child, she had a deep *love* for animals and was forever bringing home strays she found on campus. But where her family lived, they could not own pets, so her mother brought them all to the ASPCA. When she was about seven years old, she witnessed a man whipping his horse, which was pulling a cart; promptly going into action, she stopped him and "threatened to report him if he didn't leave the horse alone."

Her parents were "*loving*, but firm." Her father was a brilliant linguist who cracked the Germans' code during WWII, and he interrogated Rudolph Hess, who worked directly for Hitler. He was also a stern "disciplinarian," which was based on his upbringing. The school he attended as a boy would use "caning" as punishment. As a result, Olivia said she was "quite frightened of her father as a child, particularly when she'd be daydreaming, and he would suddenly call out to her with his penetrating voice. He was a tremendous source of insecurity." Her mother was very meticulous about the house and their diet, and insisted that the family eat healthy foods such as "yogurt, sour cream and a plentiful supply of fruits and vegetables." Her parents also instilled a work ethic in all of their children.

When she was about ten years old, her parents divorced, and this shock scared her about marriage and commitment, causing issues in her adult life. Later on, her sister got divorced, and "It left me afraid of marriage, because I'd seen so much divorce." Her fear of marriage was so deep that she found it difficult to commit to getting married. She said, "If you have never seen a relationship that lasts forever, you tend to believe it's not possible. I can still remember the terrible shock I felt when my father said he was moving away." He did end up moving, far away, and she only got to see him "once or twice a year." Olivia felt "wounded, hurt and insecure." As a reaction to her childhood experiences, she became a people-pleaser. When her parents divorced, the Australian society "frowned upon" divorced people and viewed divorce as "scandalous." Her family would be talked about, which made her the "odd girl out" with her friends' families. She always hoped her parents would get back together.

Even though she stayed with her mother, she didn't want to leave her father. Olivia never wanted her mother to know how disappointed she was over their divorce. She also became a "latchkey kid" when her brother went off to college and her sister ran off to get married. Then she channeled herself into music, writing her first song as a teenager, and struggling with her insecurities in order to sing publicly. Finally, seeing her talent, her mother sent her to a vocal coach. She went "to please her mother," but left "unimpressed." She was particularly frustrated that the teacher was trying to change her natural singing voice, "in a way she felt was unnatural."

At school, "she was so self-conscious about wearing a swimming suit in front of boys that she refused to be on the school swimming team." Her school dances were "torture, because I wasn't a natural dancer and felt I might fall over at any moment." As she grew older, she started appearing on TV, and as her popularity grew, her mother became her manager. When she was a teen, Olivia started dating a successful singer and TV personality whom her mother liked, but felt they got too serious, too soon. Olivia won a trip to England, and her mother thought it would be a good break from her young romance and that left Olivia "heartbroken." Once again, the trip to England left Olivia homesick; she dreaded the cold, rainy weather of London, and thought, "it was the grayish, dingiest place" she'd ever seen, and that everything there was "old and dismal." She "spent nights crying into her pillow" over her boyfriend back in Australia, and he publicly said he wanted to marry Olivia.

So she promptly bought a plane ticket home, and each time her mother found out about it, she would cancel the ticket. "This left Olivia furious," and the "booking and un-booking" went on for two months. Eventually, Olivia went to a lawyer to see what could be done. But she was a minor, and this left her "very angry, I was madly in *love*, and my hormones were going crazy." Her mother, however, had her own ideas for Olivia's career. While she was in London, Olivia struggled. One night a "male singer swore in front of her," and she asked him politely if he could change his language; he then had an "outburst," and she promptly "burst into tears." (father/totalitarian)

The medication she found and swallowed when she was a toddler is processed in the liver, which correlates to the emotions of anger/frustration in Traditional Chinese Medicine. As children, we fear abandonment or not fitting in, and after a family's move and/or divorce, children tend to please people out of fear. Animals give us unconditional *love*, especially when we cannot see the love within ourselves. They can also reflect our vision of ourselves if they are abandoned or abused.

As an adult, Olivia endured heartaches in relationships that may have mimicked some of her struggles as a child. We repeat lessons until we acknowledge, heal and learn from these patterns of trauma. When we finally recognize these patterns, we can understand ourselves at a deeper level in order to let go; that allows us to discover who we truly are. Olivia endured three miscarriages, which are related to kidney in Traditional Chinese Medicine, the emotion fear, the mother-child bond, and essence from parents. Miscarriages are also related to the breast cancer, because the cancer had spread to her bones (kidney) and can indicate the fear of being emotionally or physically supported.

May Sarton:

The book *May Sarton* by Margot Peters, was about the writer known as the "lesbian author." Born in Belgium, she wrote numerous books of poetry, novels, and screenplays. Her father was educated in science, consumed by his own career in the pursuit of fame. Her mother was "an artist of nervous sensibility, neurotically plagued by illnesses both real and imagined, frustrated both by her ambitions and by her husband's blind absorption in his work." Both of her parents had difficult and strained relationships with their own parents. Her fraternal grandmother died when her father was a toddler, and her mother was left with "caretakers" while her parents traveled for her father's work. When May's mother was old enough, she was sent away to school; she said she "did not *love* her mother, whose indifferences blighted her childhood."

May's parents loved each other very much, but constantly disagreed and argued. Her father George wanted to be the "child of the house" -- even when Mabel was pregnant with May. Mabel suffered from both real and imagined illnesses, and her father remained "selfish, boyish, and enthusiastic." Mabel would soon realize that a baby was an all-consuming project; she became exhausted by motherhood, and yet could not give up her career as an artist. Her mother had intense friendships with other women and later realized that "she should not have married." When May was about a year old, her mother left to stay with friends and "seldom asked after her daughter." This left May abandoned by her mother and ignored mainly by her father; she was now in a prolonged exile from both parents.

Sadly, George and Mabel, both neglected as children, had already established that pattern with their own child. Feeling abandoned and ignored, May developed the fine art of the tantrum, for which doctors "recommended plunges into cold tubs." Every time May was sent away to someone else's home, she would cling to the new caretaker, becoming "demanding and spoiled." She became overly attached to anything - "a flower, a kitten, a cloud, a butterfly, a tree." During WWI, Mabel and May fled Belgium to live in England. They were constantly on the move in search of a safe place to stay -- with family, friends, strangers, whoever would take them in.

In the meantime, May's father went to America and invented Bakelite, which made him a wealthy man; but he was tight with his money. May became ever more willful and "brattish" and constantly tested her mother. Her mother would "lock her away in a room" or "burn her fingers" when she played with matches. May became increasingly outspoken and aggressive that her mother once said, "My body is so tired.... May tires me so much that I feel sometimes that I should go mad if there were two (children). I really must think I must be a woman with an insufficiency of the 'mother' in her" .... One time "May fell ill with a severe abscess and a raging temperature," and she would say, "Me a big girl, me not cry. Daddy will be glad." Her mother would send letters to her husband in America, pleading for financial help while she suffered with May.

When May came down with the measles and was "extremely ill," the doctors finally "advised Mabel for her health to 'get rid' of May." Mabel struggled with this decision, and May pleaded, "*Love* me, mommy."

Later in life, May told her biographer a terrible story: - "My father had left my mother and me stranded in England; When my mother begged him for money. He brutally replied, 'Give May away.' My mother should not have told me this, but she did. I was a teenager. It left deep scars. I have never forgiven him." Then he finally wrote us, "Come along, both beloved, come along as quick as you can." In the rest of the letter, he said that both of them were *loved*. Her parents' relationship was filled with both torment and *love*. When May finally read this letter in 1993, she "exploded" and said, "He was acting, of course!" During May's childhood, she developed "intense attachments to other women." Her mother, who was never caressed as a child, found it impossible to give her husband -- and now her daughter -- the "physical love they craved." Mabel was "very wrapped up in trying to please, and Father and daughter competed fiercely for Mabel, and George won. May turned hungrily to other mothers."

May received many letters from people who raised her and understood her situation at home. These letters of *love* confused her. "If mommy and daddy *loved* her, then why was she so often lonely and alone? It must be her fault." When Mabel wrote letters to May, they hinted of blackmail, "Be a good girl, so mommy won't fret." This only wracked May with guilt. The girl was passed around so much she would "attach herself immediately to anyone who was kind." She felt so guilty when she wrote to her mother, she'd "underline her good behavior." May also felt the "nervous need to be constantly moving from place to place. These were survival techniques." After May's birth, her mother endured two other pregnancies; both were boys who died shortly after birth.

Around the age of 13, May and her parents traveled back to Europe, and they enrolled May in a school in Belgium, leaving her friends and what little security she had behind in America. She struggled in school with her French; her teacher "terrorized students by the ferocity of her anger, tears, and smiles." During this time, May was examined by a psychologist who would look into his patients' eyes to diagnose them. May was "deeply offended and frightened by his diagnosis.... the fright took the form of a waking nightmare;" for a while, she was "convinced that I was going mad."

As a child, she suffered from frequent migraines, stomach issues, and tantrums.

In an article in the *Baltimore Sun* titled *May Sarton's life: Defining a Place,* Victoria Brownworth wrote, "she was born to parents who *loved* the idea of a child more than the child itself." As a result, Sarton spent much of her childhood living "haphazardly among her parents' friends." This caused her a lifetime of emotional issues in which she was searching for *love,* companionship, relationships, and this affected her writing. May's mother also had breast cancer, which could be attributed to the fact that she had been abandoned herself -- while she was raised with "caretakers."

May had breast cancer and depression, as well as diverticulitis. Her diet was typical for that time period, rich in animal products such as meat and dairy. This would have increased the inflammation in her body and brain. Diverticulitis occurs in the colon/large intestine and, in Traditional Chinese Medicine, is related to the emotions of grief and sadness. Depression increases when the brain is suffering from inflammation. The breast cancer is due to the abandonment from her mother.

Sondra Locke:

According to *Wikipedia,* Sondra Locke had two abortions and a tubal ligation during her relationship with Clint Eastwood. The reason for this: "I'd feel sorry for any child who had me as their mother." Eastwood also suggested at the time that children did not fit into their lifestyle, while he also got two other women pregnant during his relationship with Locke.

In her book, *The Good, The Bad & The Very Ugly*, she talks about her upbringing in rural Tennessee. Her parents were "simple and uneducated," and she had a hard time associating with them. When her parents fought, she would go out on the porch and cover her ears so she couldn't hear the screaming and yelling. (Ears are related to the kidney and the emotion fear in Traditional Chinese Medicine. Fear is also a factor in PTSD fright/freezing.) Her mother would threaten to leave Sondra's father.

When Sondra was young, a strange man took her and her mother to a hotel. She didn't understand why, but would remember that her mother, upon occasion, would run away. Sondra felt like she was in an "extended summer camp, waiting to be picked up. There had to be something more." As part of her escape from her life, Sondra used to read a lot. This used to annoy her mother, who would say, "You read too much. It's not good for you." During her "dark memories" of her parents, Sondra remembered that her mother hated being called mother, so she called her "Pah-yee" for Phyllis. Her brother would torment June bugs by tying strings on their legs and flying them like kites, which Sondra hated.

Her grandmother, who lived with them, was the one she called Mamma. When Sondra was about five years old, she caught her fingers in an old wringer washer, and when she screamed, it was Mamma who came to help her. She said that "Mamma was my favorite person then." Sondra was fascinated with movies, because they allowed her to escape to a magical world far away and out of her mundane life. She spent the "happiest times" of her life there, in the "magic window that could take me where everything meant something, where women were beautiful and lead bold lives." This is where she met her friend who would change her life forever.

Gordon was a friend she met in school who left a lifelong impression on her. He lived in a world that she had dreamt about: "acting," which was her ultimate escape from reality. Gordon himself created this wonderful escape from reality. Once he said, "I can remember the hot sun, and that I was very hurt and had been crying because of something my brother and his gang in the 'Post 80' had done to me. I was running.... when suddenly I saw a kitten." He got a rope to hang the kitten, and then he heard a voice telling him he was the kitten, and that's when he heard the word of God. He describes two people within him; without Number Two, "I might have killed myself a long time ago. Number Two comes from God." He, too, used the movies and theater as an escape, and his great-aunt performed in vaudeville. Gordon was fascinated by illusions of all kinds.

Sondra spent a lot of time being safe and living in an illusional made-up world with Gordon, who could create every fantasy she could ever think up and make it real. He said, "I could feel God all around me." It gave him a sense of peace and euphoria. Gordon had an independent strength about him that was unshakable, and Sondra admired him for it. When he met her family, he told her, "You are absolutely nothing like your family." He also noticed that the man she called "Daddy" was not her father. When she was young, she found a picture of herself with the name "Sondra Smith" written on it, but with "Smith" crossed off. When she found her birth certificate, she saw the name "Raymond Smith. I knew it would do no good to ask my mother; she never answered questions, so I begged her Momma to tell me the truth." Her Momma said he was in the Army, and it never worked out between him and her mother. Sondra knew in her heart that they had never married. Gordon said to her, "I know what, you're illegitimate, Sondra." This shocked her. He tried to comfort her and told her that this made her "special."

Gordon felt that his father didn't care about him and never appreciated his talents as an artist. He spent days making a drawing, and his father said that he had copied it. As he and Sondra sat there in dismay, his father said, "Oh, why don't you go and kill a bunny rabbit and throw it down the sewer." Gordon was angry and said, "Let's get out of here." And his father yelled back, "Don't you talk to me like that; I'll stomp you." Gordon said, "I've been hearing I'm going to be stomped since I was three." One day Gordon had rescued a baby rabbit, which he had left in his father's care. His father left the baby rabbit in the hot sun, and by the time Gordon got home, the rabbit was dead. He made Gordon put the dead rabbit down the sewer and used a strap for punishment. All of this trauma highlighted Gordon's intuitive ability. He'd always been there for Sondra, and encouraged her, and he could see that she would make a fine actress. But when Sondra finally graduated high school, she felt "lost."

When she was in a play in college, her parents decided to attend, which gave Sondra an "unexplainable anxiety." During one of the "highly charged" scenes, her mother yelled out, "Hey you. Leave that girl alone, you hear me?" It was as if her mother was being triggered. After a series of "little abuses," their relationship blew up, and her mother said, "If you don't do exactly what I tell you, you can pack your bags, girl, and get outta here. This is my house, not yours." Sondra left and went to her cousin's house. No one even called to inquire about her whereabouts, which only added to her hurt.

It was only when her mother came to reclaim the TV, that she saw her. Her brother held her down on the bed as her mother unplugged the TV set and left. Sondra was screaming and pleading with her. Sondra felt "she had come to hurt and humiliate me." She vowed that "the television was the last thing-literally and symbolically-she would ever take from me." In thirty years, she only had maybe a "handful of conversations or short visits with my mother. It made no sense for any of us to spend our lives pretending to have relationships that did not really exist." Even when she moved away from home, she attempted to patch up her relationship with her mother, only to end up feeling "humiliated."

This disconnected relationship between her, and her mother followed her in her adult relationships throughout most of her life. How can you learn to connect to people when you can't connect to the woman who gave birth to you?

As women, we are built to have children. It's part of our nature. I know firsthand the anger and the betrayal that someone feels having an abortion. Even though she thought the abortions was for the best, pregnancy will always affect a woman, deep down inside. This is one of the deepest forms of rejection a woman can go through.

Sondra passed away from breast cancer that had metastasized to her bones. In Traditional Chinese

Medicine, the bone is related to kidney. It also correlates with your essence from parents, fertility and the emotion fear.

I find that children who don't want to hear will eat crunchy food to drown out the yelling or screaming of their parents. This is one of the behaviors that Sondra used as a child.

Cynthia Nixon:

An article by Marc Myers called *Cynthia Nixon Is Her Mother's Daughter,* for wsj.com Sept. 8, 2020, says, "My mother taught me to fib with a straight face." Her mother worked on game shows as a writer, and coached contestants for the show "To Tell the Truth." Cynthia got her chance to be on the show when she was 7. Her mother was an actor, writer, and coach for many years in the television industry; her father was unable to hold a job due to his depression issues. He also had a "terrifying temper," during which "he did a lot of screaming, and my mother did a lot of crying." Her parents ended up separating when she was 6. It was such a relief for her and her mother that they "danced around the apartment" when he left.

"My mother was as much a mom as she was my director and acting coach. Narrative was a big deal in my house." Anytime Cynthia and her mother went to plays, movies, or read books, they would analyze "what worked, what didn't, what they could have done better." (Parentification, buddies.) So, it was a natural fit that Cynthia acted when she was a child and later went into directing, because her mother had trained her during her whole life. As a teenager, her mother told her that when she was younger; she had an illegal abortion. Cynthia stated on her Twitter account: "It was too harrowing for her to discuss." Cynthia also said: "My wife had a legal abortion after we found out her pregnancy was not viable."

In an article written in the *Cayman Compass* by Norma Connolly, Actress *Nixon Shares Mother's Battle at Breast Cancer Gala* dated October 2, 2016, "Her mother found a lump in 1979 when she was 49 years old, and Ms. Nixon was 13." Her abortion may explain some of the emotional reasons behind her breast cancer diagnosis, as well as the struggles of being a single parent. Being brave enough to talk about abortion is a challenging and necessary healing process, which may have helped her mother survive another 35 years after her original diagnosis."

In an article in the 2017 edition of *Basque Luxury Magazine,* Cynthia said, "I grew up in a family where I wasn't allowed to be angry a lot, or express big emotions. I was told to behave. And I could get out of that strictness by acting."

On a podcast called *Little Known Facts with Ilana Levine, Episode 3,* during her interview, Cynthia said about her childhood with her mother, "There was not a lot of kid stuff." Her mother enjoyed film, theater, and reading. "We didn't talk about feelings. We didn't talk about my imaginary friends," only "the imaginary people that we see up on stage." Cynthia discovered that when you act and show emotions, you get "accolades and get paid." Her father had his struggles and was previously married, and had two boys he couldn't support, so he disconnected from them. Later, as her father was dying with emphysema (lung in Traditional Chinese Medicine is related to the emotions grief and sadness), he finally apologized to his sons.

She stated in the interview that she had developed stage fright. "One of the things I can't bear now is to stand off-stage and wait." She wants to "bolt." This sensation is part of PTSD, the "flight" part. This may have triggered her restrained emotions from childhood, when her father was screaming, and her mother was crying. The stage is where she can freely express her character's feelings, since she felt restrained as a child by her own emotions. She mentioned a character she played in the film *James White*, the mother, who is dying of cancer. "There is so much I have in common with that character, and there's so much my mother has in common with that character," and it "felt like a second skin." She later described her relationship with her mother as, "I was the affair that got my mom out of her bad marriage." (Parentification)

In her interview with oprahmag.com, entitled *Ratched's Cynthia Nixon Says the Subway is Her Favorite Place to be in the World,* by Melissa Goldberg, September 17, 2020. Cynthia stated, "I crave anything with cheese; the more, the better. It's just cheese, cheese, cheese."

Suppression of emotions stifles a child's ability to regulate their own emotions, and they will seek out other avenues of expression, such as acting. She stated that she craves cheese (dairy), which substitutes for the original addiction to breast milk and reinforces the mother-child bond.

I have had many patients tell me that when they are upset, they turn to dairy as comfort food, and as discussed earlier, it provides a sedative and sugar to activate the feel-good hormones, just like mother's milk. So, I asked my patients, before they grab their soothing dairy products, ask your "inner child," why do you need mommy right now?

Carly Simon:

Carly was born into a wealthy New York family; her father was a co-owner of the publishing company Simon & Schuster. In her book, *Boys in the Trees, a*

Memoir, she talked about her childhood growing up in a house with two older sisters and a younger brother. Her father came from a very talented family with a history of mental illness; he also served during WWI and was a talented piano player. Her mother was the receptionist at Simon & Schuster. When Carly was born, her parents were expecting a boy and only picked out the name Carl, so they just added a "y." When she was three years old, her younger brother Peter was born; her father had a "nervous collapse" and was in the hospital for about five weeks. Her parents entertained a lot of famous people and were active in social circles. Carly felt that her father doted on her two older sisters but was distant with her, and never really paid much attention to her. She described their relationship as "remote and uneasy."

During her childhood, her parents we so busy that she spent most of her time with her grandmother and nanny. She felt so close to her nanny that Carly would steal her mother's jewelry and give it to her. This happened so often, the nanny would return it to her mother by the end of the day. Carly felt that her nanny should have the same beautiful things that her mother had.

When Carly was about six, she was groomed by a neighborhood boy who sexually abused her for several years. However, she felt that she *loved* him and would do anything to protect their relationship, which occurred each summer at their home in Connecticut. This left her feeling withdrawn, and she described herself as an "anxious child, jittery, insecure," and was "scared to be alone" and "scared of the dark." As her insomnia issues increased, she would "make up strange games in her head to force myself to fall back asleep." She stated, "One of my most fun fantasies had as its setting a naval warship on a black, cold, rough sea." In Traditional Chinese Medicine, water, cold and black are all related to the kidney and the emotion fear and sex, and sexuality. Her abuse took place at the pool house (water/ kidney/fear)

During this time, a family friend would gather all the children to perform in a play, and Carly started to stutter. She said that when she was attempting to say her lines, her "throat closed up," and she felt as if "a snake, which had been coiled and asleep around her esophagus, had suddenly reared up, strangling the words." In Traditional Chinese Medicine, the lung opens up into the throat and is related to the emotions grief and sadness. The snake in Chinese culture is about control. Sigmund Freud, the famous neurologist and founder of psychoanalysis would say that the snake was a phallic symbol for the penis.

The Throat Chakra is responsible for communication and self-expression, and the ability to speak the truth. She was choking to get the words or the truth out. Isn't a play a lie? Even though she had so much trouble speaking because of her stuttering and stammering, they still didn't drop her from the play, which only increased her feelings of anxiety and self-consciousnesses. The day before the play, she would fantasize about falling out of a tree where she had spent much of her summers playing and breaking every bone in her body so she couldn't perform. This is what PTSD looks like in a child. The anger is related to the liver in Traditional Chinese Medicine (trees), and the (broken bones) are related to fear and the kidney, and sex. These are the scars of PTSD, and the activation of fight, flight, and freezing playing out in her fantasy.

When she was 11 years old, her parents noticed that Carly was having increased stammering and struggles in school, so they sent her to a music therapist. During a session, he sang to her, "Ginger Rogers, Fred Astaire, has a man ever touched you down there?" And finally, she sang back, "I stood so tall, and he did stare/then he sat me on his chair." She was about six or seven when she and Billy would go down to the pool house at night, where the sexual abuse occurred for several years. Her parents also took her to a nude beach when she was five years old, where everyone, friends, family, including her two older sisters, was nude; she felt so ashamed.

She would do anything to protect Billy, because she thought this was *love* and was captivated by his attention, which she had always wanted from both her parents. Unfortunately, her parents were so wrapped up in the life they had created with parties and appearances that Carly was the odd child out. Her parents had the attitude to treat her abuse as if nothing ever happened, and it was not publicly discussed in order to keep up appearances. Also, during her childhood, there were parties at their summer home where Carly witnessed the adults doing some uninhibited sexual behavior. It was her mother, who was cavorting in the bushes with various people.

When she was about ten years old, her parents decided that their son needed a male role model/ babysitter named Ronny, a local college student, and he moved into the house. This put a strain on her father's health, and her sisters told her that "when mommy and daddy kissed, it was nothing more than a show." Ronny gave Carly's mom all the *love* and attention that she ever dreamed of, and her dutiful wife and mother role started to slack. Carly felt that "Ronny had stolen her away, and all I knew was that if daddy had never been mine, mommy wasn't mine any more, either." This increased the family's awkwardness, and her father became more engrossed in his work and more withdrawn and miserable.

Her mother's boyfriend was even spying on the girls in the bathroom. This increased stress caused Carly to "act out" towards Ronny, often punching him in the crotch. He was drafted into the Army and stationed in Germany, and while he was gone, it appeared that her parents were getting along -- until her mother had planned a trip to Europe by herself. "Ten days later, her daddy suffered his first heart attack," and her mother didn't come home for almost two months. Carly, at the age of ten, became worried that her father might die. Death in Traditional Chinese Medicine is related to the kidney and fear. When her mother finally returned, she acted as if nothing had ever happened, and eventually, Ronny returned home, moving back in on the third floor. Her mother said, "Because daddy's snoring is really bad now," she too moved to the third floor of the house.

By the time she was in her early teens, Carly was "fearing that daddy could disappear at any second. I became frightened to *love* him," creating once again the perfect circuit of mutual rejection. Her father had been emotionally and physically sick for a year, which "terrified" her, and then when she was 15, her father passed away.

This is, unfortunately, an example of what can happen to a child when they been emotionally abandoned, left out as the odd child since her own needs were not able to be met by either parent, who suffered from their shortcomings. Carly has suffered from osteopenia, which affects the bone and is related to kidney and fear, sex, and the essence of parents in TCM and breast cancer, the nourishment between mother and child.

Suzanne Somers:

In her book *Keeping Secrets*, she wrote: "I am an adult child of an alcoholic. My childhood and that of my brothers and sister was robbed by a terrible and painful disease no one ever wanted to talk about, including me." Her dad was an alcoholic, and her parents would "argue and be abusive to each other. Eventually, all of us children joined in the violence. I listened to my parents scream at each other all night long. My mother's personality changed. She is a sweet, non-violent woman. It was not natural for her to yell and scream. When you live with an alcoholic, his main thing is to beat you down. As long as you don't have confidence, you won't leave." A mother's job is to *love*, nurture and protect her children, and in a house with an alcoholic; you can't do that. There is nothing normal in a household with an alcoholic; they seem to blame everyone as the source of the problem but fail to see themselves and their role.

When we've been traumatized and haven't healed, we pick a spouse or a partner we can rescue, because we perceive that this as *love*. We have watched our parents or caretakers rescue their partners, and we end up mimicking the same behavior. We must learn to love ourselves first and foremost in order to share that love with someone else. It's common to see women trapped in a relational situation in order to survive. Fearing the ability to make enough money, or fearing the person they're in a relationship with, can cause people to stay. As a child watches two parents struggling with their unresolved trauma, they cannot view what healthy self-love or healthy boundaries look like.

Wanda Sykes:

According to *Wikipedia*: Wanda came from a conservative military family. When she was young, she was very outspoken -- to the point where her parents were worried when a guest would come to the house. Since Wanda at times would say something inappropriate, her parents sent her off to her grandparents when people visited in order to avoid any embarrassment. There were times that Wanda was even paid to keep silent. She started working at NSA but found the job unfulfilling, and so pursued her real *love*, comedy.

In the article in *The Guardian* dated November 25, 2018, *Wanda Sykes on Why She Had to Quit Roseanne – But Still Has Empathy for its Star*, by Amy Nickolson: "Her parents were deeply religious, and Sykes didn't come out until her 40s; she has said her mother was devastated and asked her to stay closeted. When she did come out, her mother did not go to her wedding. But, over time, her parents have grown to embrace her wife and kids, thanks in part to the aunts and uncles who prodded them to 'choose *love* over intolerance.'" Nevertheless, her parents weren't supportive of her career choice of comedy, and as they watched their daughter get booed at an open mic night, her mom said, "It's OK." Afterwards, as consolation, her mother added, "You have a good government job." Her parents couldn't believe that the daughter they had raised with their conservative values would throw away a good, steady salary to become a standup comic!"

In her NPR interview with Terry Gross, called *Wanda Sykes Loves Stand-Up: That's Where 'I Can Be Free'* Wanda mentioned that she had a double mastectomy and estrogen-positive breast cancer. The double mastectomy represents cutting off the nourishment to mother and child emotionally. Many breast cancer patients I have met are on an estrogen blocker for 5-7 years -- only to have the breast cancer reoccur. This can happen because most patients are still consuming dairy products, and many eat low-fat. In dairy, the lower the fat content, the higher the estrogen content, so when the patients stop the estrogen blocker, that no longer stops blocking the estrogen in the dairy.

Giuliana Rancic:

Her book, *Going Off Script*, tells how Rancic grew up in Italy; when she was about six years old, her family moved to America. As they were flying over, she witnessed her mother's "utter terror" when the plane had to make an emergency landing, thus began Giuliana's fear of flying. At school, she couldn't speak English, and no one could pronounce her name, so they renamed her Julie – along with all the other Julies. Now she had lost her identity. In Italy, she was the blonde one, an anomaly, which drew people to her; in America, she was just another blond-haired Julie. She went from being the center of attention in a large and doting family to just being average. Giuliana also became a latchkey kid who was terrified by the local news, on which she was fixated. She repeatedly called her mother at work to come home and comfort her. To compound the issue, she was at the mercy of her older siblings, who would make her watch horror movies, and then tell her that the movies were based on true stories.

During one of her trips back to her native Italy, when she was around nine years old, she witnessed a murder; after this episode, she asked her mother for a pacifier. Her mother took her to the pharmacy and asked for a "pacifier for a nine-year-old." This is an excellent, but unfortunate, example of someone so traumatized that they revert to the original oral fixation, suckling. Suckling at mommy's breast is the safest place to be, because you'll get your tryptophan (sedative) and lactose (happy drug) to make you feel better - all while in your mother's warm and comforting arms. As Rancic notes, "The pacifier was just my way of getting a tranquilizer." She only needed the pacifier while she was in Italy.

When her older sister Monica was around 13 years old, she was diagnosed with scoliosis and needed surgery. When she came out of surgery; and her family was in the hospital room, Giuliana witnessed her sister crying out in pain and wanting to kill herself by jumping out of the window. That left an indelible mark on the whole family, especially Giuliana. Because her sister had the attitude that the world owed her, and her parents were guilt-ridden and would buy her whatever she wanted. All the while, she was stealing money from family members! Her parents were also overprotective in certain aspects of her life, and under- protective in other aspects.

After their trips back to Italy, Giuliana would return two weeks into the next semester of school; so every summer, she'd have to catch up with the rest of the class. When she was about 13, she started "borrowing" people's cars for joy rides, leading to run-ins with the local police. At school, the nurse was giving annual physicals, and noticed that Giuliana's back was curved, and she was sent home. She was so freaked out about it all she could think about when her sister was in the hospital, reeling in pain, wanting to kill herself. At that time, she was lucky and didn't need surgery, but as her body grew, it started to betray her. Her back pain increased as she grew unevenly when she started high school, which only increases her insecurities. Finally, when she was in college, her back was so bad that she needed corrective surgery and underwent the same surgery that she had watched her sister endure. She was in tremendous pain, and it took several months to recover from the surgery.

According to *Wikipedia*: Rancic had difficulties getting pregnant and suffered the loss of a child through miscarriage. She also went through unsuccessful IVF treatments. She and her husband have one son, by a surrogate.

The spine (bone) in Traditional Chinese Medicine is related to the kidneys, the emotion fear, and infertility issues. When the spine cannot support the body properly, you can ask, "Did she have a fear of not being emotionally supported?"

Shannon Doherty:

In her book *Badass: A Hard-Earned Guide to Living Life with Style and (The Right) Attitude,* Shannon Doherty wrote, "My sense of security was shattered, though, when my mom Rosa almost died when I was ten, and then my dad, Tom, got very sick." Her father endured many health issues; she asked her mom to stay at home and be her father's caregiver. At the age of 18, Shannon assumed the role of breadwinner for her family. "I'll tell ya, it's a lot of pressure for an eighteen-year-old kid, -and the feeling that I could lose my dad at any moment was a scary one." She stated: "I was not only afraid of losing my beloved father and mother, but also carrying the worry about what would happen to all of us if something were to happen to me." (Parentification)

Those burdens will affect your life at 18, and the stress will appear in many different ways. The inner child will crave nourishment from mother, which will eventually alter a person's eating habits.

As a child, you're constantly going to wonder when things are going to get better. When is your mom or dad going to leave, or die? The more we get exposed to the dysfunction, the more it seems to become normal behavior, and when we leave home, we'll seek out the same pattern because we associate dysfunction with our parents' *love* and survival. Even though it's NOT love at all; yet we did survive. When children are exposed to these patterns of stress and dysfunction, they're going to crave nourishment in any form to help ease the pain and the feelings of abandonment. What's more natural to nourish a baby than breast milk? Since it's not practical or socially acceptable to latch on to mother's breast, especially after a certain age, the body craves the next best thing to soothe itself, and that's dairy.

I have met several women with estrogen-driven breast cancer tell me that the one food they cannot give up is dairy.

There are many types of traumas between mother and child that may well contribute to stuffing emotions. When these emotions are neither addressed nor resolved, that will lead to improper lifelong eating habits that can contribute to health issues such as cancers.

Jane Fonda:

In Jane's book *My Life Story So Far,* she wrote, "Mother wasn't with us much more...I had stopped paying attention much to her being away...Even when she was, Grandma Seymour would be in charge of us. But even though I *loved* her, I don't remember ever running joyfully into her arms the way my own grandchildren do with me." Jane's mother was hospitalized for quite some time for a kidney operation, and when Jane visited her in the hospital, her mother said, "They almost cut me in half." As a child, Jane herself even spent a lot of time in hospitals with various illnesses.

While all of this was going on, her father, Henry, suffered from what was probably PTSD and had fits of anger and "black moods." He was also busy working and wasn't around much. Jane tried to do her best being the peacekeeper of the family. Her mother finally told her that she and Henry were getting a divorce. Jane's mother showed her scars from all her previous surgeries, which left Jane in shock; she believed that was why they were getting divorced.

Jane's mother became increasingly saddened, worried about the lack of income, and the rationed canned food; she was eventually sent to a mental hospital. One day, her mother came for a visit, and Jane refused to see her out of anger and hurt. Shortly after the visit, her mother killed herself. Later in her own life, Jane learned that her mother had been physically and sexually abused as a child, and had had a kidney operation with Traditional Chinese medicine related to the emotion fear and sexual issues.

In an article called "Jane Fonda: 'I'm 80! I keep pinching myself. I can't believe it!'" on theguardian.com by Sophie Haywood, Jane commented, Mother's "life was socially privileged, her home life was agony, and her mother, Frances Ford Seymour, killed herself in a psychiatric hospital. (Fonda was 12, and only found out that her mother's death was suicide by reading a movie magazine – nobody ever spoke to her about it.) Jane herself was also sexually abused. In her memoirs, she writes movingly about the concept of disembodiment – how it took her until the age of 62 to fully inhabit her own body." She also reflected on her cosmetic surgeries, linked her plastic surgery to "sexual abuse," and comments that when she sees the face "of a woman who has made herself into a mask, I always think to myself... I wonder, I wonder." Jane had her "breast implants taken out, and has also had several facelifts, of which she says she is 'not proud.'"

Jane has had breast cancer. Her hip replacements, which bone is related to the kidney and fear and sexual issues. They are also in the Root Chakra, which can indicate mistrust, anxiety, depression, fear, instability, as well as feeling grounded or rooted in one's life. When a woman has implant surgery to enlarge her breasts, she may be linking that to nourishing, or trying to fulfill the missing nourishment between, mother and child. When a woman has breasts removed, they cut off or remove the toxic breast or toxic nourishment that goes from mother to child.

We all alter who we are, especially when we are looking for *love* in someone else. We mimic so many qualities of this person or that person in order to be liked or *loved,* that we lose ourselves and forget about the beautiful person who resides within us. Our broken inner child needs us to be supportive in so many ways, and yet we ignore ourselves for someone of no importance.

Bette Davis:

In Bette Davis' biography, The *Girl Who Walked Home Alone,* by Charlotte Chandler, "She believed that parents had to be firm, because only through imposing a strict code of values would your child know you *loved* him or her. Until your children hate you, you haven't been a good parent. Constructive fear. Your children, sometimes you have to put the fear of God in them. You must!" Bette continued, "My father handed me my family to support when I was nineteen, the assumption being, I suppose that I was now old enough to become the man of the house. Too much of my life has been squandered fighting self-pity, a battle which I should have won easily but instead lost." Bette's mother, Ruthie, had shown an interest in acting, but was OK with the role of housewife. Her father, Harlow, was accepted into Harvard Law School when her mother and father got married. Bette had always thought there must have been a witch in her family's history. "I was at least born like a witch: A bolt of lightning hit a tree in front of the house the moment I was born. Mother told me it happened between a flash of lightning and a clap of thunder."

Her father never planned on having a family, especially so soon, nine months after the honeymoon. When her mother told her father that she was pregnant, "he blamed her for being 'inefficient' and suggested that she 'do' something about it. 'It' being me. He regarded the 'it' that was me as being entirely mother's doing. Her fault." During her parents' honeymoon, there was a water shortage at the hotel, "Mother couldn't take proper precautions, whatever they were in those days." And her "father went into an absolute rage, raising hell with everybody in the hotel, including my mother. My father never did forgive my mother for her 'carelessness.'" Even Ruthie's mother-in-law warned her about her new husband. "He will make your life miserable, my dear. You can be certain." And at her parents' wedding, when the guests threw the rice, Harlow turned and said, "God damn, you--I'll get you for this!" Bette remembered her father was "a very brilliant, disagreeable man. I could not recall one moment of affection between my parents during my early years of life, when my father was still around." When Bette's sister Bobby was born, "I admit that Bobby's arrival on the scene wasn't anything I felt I'd been consulted about, and I felt not only should I have been, but if I had been, I most certainly would have said, skip it." (Losing the baby status). She didn't see Bobby as a necessary addition to the family, but as time grew, she got "rather used to her." Bette, who was young when her sister came into her life, treated Bobby as her own personal doll. Her mother had to explain the situation, and Bette never wanted to hurt her mother, so she "committed to protecting Bobby."

After her father graduated from law school, he spent less and less time at home. Her mother was unhappy in the marriage and had committed herself for a short time to a sanatorium to recover. It was there her mother was encouraged to take up photography as a hobby. "There was no real communication of any kind between my father and the rest of us. None of us could break through the wall of ice around Harlow Morrow Davis." This affected her sister "terribly," and Bette "simply stayed out of his way." Yet he *loved* to play "Santa Claus at Christmas." And "was generous to a fault." Later Bette learned that "this was what guilty husbands do. I believe that my father was faithfully unfaithful. One mistress at a time." Ruthie and Harlow separated when Bette was seven. Bette was happy about the news, but her sister was "utterly demolished."

(According to *Wikipedia*, Bette was sent off for three years to boarding school. When she was around 13, her mother took the girl's school tuition and paid for her own tuition in a photography school in New York.)

Chandler went on to say about Bette, as her mother attempted to move on with her life, "she made the fatal mistake of asking Bobby and me if we like this or that man as our father. We never did. Heavens no! we'd say." At the time, the girls never understood what impact this would have on their mother's life, because their mother struggled and took several jobs to make ends meet. When Bette was twelve, she dressed up as Santa Claus and got too close to the candles on the tree. She caught her beard on fire and burnt and blistered her face. (Fire is related to the emotions love/joy in Traditional Chinese Medicine. She played Santa, just like her father did.) Her mother took excellent care of her to ensure proper healing from her burns, but her "skin was never the same again." (The skin itself is related to the emotions grief/sadness.) She was self-conscious of her appearance and her body that if she "caught a glimpse of herself in the mirror without clothes on, all by myself in my room, I blushed. Strangely enough, when I was about eleven, I posed nude for a woman sculptor because we needed the money."

When her mother moved them to New York, they had to attend a new high school. "I remember the pain of being a "wallflower" at the school dance. As she recalled this memory, "she winced when she spoke." She felt that the boy who asked her to dance did so as a "mercy-dance." Traumatized, she ran home "to the security of Ruthie's waiting arms." Her mother was everything to her, and prepared Bette in every way for the next dance. Hair, makeup, new dress, so much so that the students thought she was a brand-new student and that she was "there for the first time." She ended up being the belle of the ball.

The only thing her mother never prepared her for was sex. She never learned about the birds and the bees from Ruthie. "I was a total dolt. I don't have the foggiest notion what the birds and the bees do, though I have had my share of experiences with what men and women do." She could talk to her mother about anything except the birds and the bees, because Ruthie was her "best friend." (Parentification). With her lack of knowledge about sex, at the ripe old age of thirteen, she kissed a boy. Later at home, "a nagging thought crept into my mind. Was I pregnant?" She couldn't ask her mother out of fear of "disgracing Ruthie." So she felt that the best plan of action was to wait. "A few days later, my tummy seemed to swell, and I was convinced that I was pregnant. My horror was indescribable. Then when I got my first period, I absolutely thought I was dying. I don't ever want to experience terror like that again." Ruthie finally "explained the facts of life to me."

She changed the spelling of her name because a neighbor said she would stand out and be different. When she wrote her father about the name change and how she felt about him, he replied, "You'll get over it." Bette thought, "I believe so much of what I am, I owe to his negativity and lack of interest, as well as my own insubordinate nature." Nevertheless, she was happy about the name change and that she was going to stand out. "The person I wanted 'to show' was not my dear, doting mother, who appreciated everything about me, but my impossible-to-please father, who simply didn't care. I was never able to gain Daddy's full attention, but I never gave up trying until he died—and not even then."

After her mother took her to a play, Bette felt that she had channeled the main character, and she felt scenes were being played out right before her eyes. She knew at that moment that she wanted to be an actress. Her mother wrote her father to tell her the exciting news of Bette wishing to become an actress, and her father wrote back, "She'll earn more money as a secretary, and besides, Betty will never be a successful actress. She doesn't have what it takes." As usual, Daddy inspired me - to prove him wrong." He would always write to Bette with the name Betty. She used her anger towards her dad to fuel her career, and, looking back, possibly that same fuel burned her marriages. While she trained as an actress, she learned typing and secretarial work, which helped support her family. When she went for her first interview into acting school, she was so nervous, "My tryout was an abomination." Bette had trouble functioning with people who "doubts my ability to do something." She went home furious. She carried this hurt from her rejection for years, just like her father's rejection. During her childhood, they moved several times. Her mother finally got Bette accepted into a famous acting school in New York even though she did not have the money. "She opened the door to my dream, as she always had. But Ruthie never pushed me through that door. I had enough push for the whole family." The family moved yet again. She said, "An actress's life is one of such utter dependency."

The book *Dark Victory: The Life of Bette Davis* by Ed Sikov, talks about Bette's childhood. When Bobby was born, Ruthie was in labor for 21 hours and never let her forget it. "Bobby grew deaf to the 'oft-repeated horror' story. Ruthie never identified with Bobby in any way." Bobby was too much of a mirror to Ruthie's depression issues, so "it was easier for her to take credit for Bette's success and remind Bobby of how difficult she'd been to produce." Ruthie was "an emotional drain, as well as a financial one. The rewards flowed to Bette's mother, not from her, for most of her life." (Parentification). At her mother's 72nd birthday party, Bette showed up wearing a maid's outfit. It was only after her mother's death that she could speak freely about her. Bette felt that her mother was a "selfless-turned-selfish woman who had dominated her life through four marriages.

But Ruthie's departure for eternity only served to kick in Bette's guilt."

Because of her mother's resentment, Bette to learned to resent her sister and treated her "like a dog." (From the impact of losing the "baby" status.) Later in Bette's life, a box of letters that her mother wrote to a friend was found. Bette was terrified to read them and asked a friend to be there for support. In the letters, Ruthie referred to Bette as "a chore and a pain," calling her "Queen Bee." This enraged Bette, because she had supported her mother throughout her life. And Bette had struggled with obsessive-compulsive behavior, anger, self-pity, and loneliness.

Bette was a chain smoker. In Traditional Chinese Medicine, chain smoking is related to the emotions of grief/sadness. She also tended to seek romance from many suitors; one of her earliest boyfriends proposed, but only under the condition that she quit acting. She was engaged "for three days." I believed that romance and *love,* when found in the right person, would last forever. In my case, it lasted for-never. For-never is the opposite of forever." When she lived at home and started getting serious with a boy, she would "go off the deep end," so her mother would invite the boy over as a "houseguest." Bette's "over-exposure" to these fellas would break her *love* spell, and she would ask her mother when they were going to leave.

She had spent her life looking and longing for daddy's approval and had four marriages and numerous affairs. When Bette was under contract at the studio, the studio would pay for abortions to keep the good image of the actors; Bette had several abortions during this time. As adults, we'll repeat the self-abandonment that we learned as children, such as rejection of her children(abortions) to please others, possibly for the men in her life and the studio executives. Since her father seemed disinterested in his own children. Towards the end of her life, she suffered with breast cancer and after her surgery suffered from strokes. The breast cancer would reflect her unresolved emotional issues with both her mother and her own children and abortions. The strokes and the paralysis of her limbs would correlate to her losing her ability to move forward in her life both emotionally and physically. She also was a heavy smoker for years which reflects her ongoing struggle with grief and sadness.

Peter Criss:

In Peter's book *Makeup to Breakup,* he talks about his early childhood. He was born breech and was two months premature, which might have contributed to the many illnesses he faced as a child. For most of his childhood, he was either sick or accident-prone.

He also had an accident where a dog bit his face and Peter was rushed to the hospital. During the repair to his face, the doctors never gave him any anesthesia, which he said felt like a "thousand bee stings." After this accident, his mother kept a watchful eye on him, and he spent many nights in his mother's bed watching TV with her. He felt that he and his mother had a deep relationship that was more than mother and son (parentification); he always felt a strong need never to let her down. When he attended Catholic school, he was victimized and abused, and in public school, he was beaten by gang members.

In an online article on ultimateclassicrock.com called *Peter Criss Talks About Childhood in Excerpt from New Book.* By Billy Dukes, published September 10, 2012. "The Catman shares that he was a sickly baby born backwards into an immigrant family troubled by drinking and infidelity." He goes on to share, I "was struck by seemingly every possible illness…often injured in bizarre ways." His, "father was illiterate" and "floated in and out of his life." His grandmother "beat him regularly." And he used to take "showers together" with grandfather.

INTERVIEW: Peter Criss (solo artist and Ex-Kiss), written by Mark Diggins, mentions him getting ready to watch a movie with Oreos and "my milk." And he says, "I'm like a 15-year-old kid."

When people have unresolved traumas, they crave the same foods that gave them comfort as a child. They may also have been frozen in time by their trauma, and so might have similar behaviors and eating habits that are age-appropriate for the age at which the original trauma occurred.

Ingrid Bergman:

Her book, *Ingrid Bergman: My Story* by Ingrid Bergman and Alan Burgess, tells about how, when she was three years old, her mother died. Her father wanted her to become an opera singer, which was not what Ingrid wanted to do. When she was 13, her father died, and she was sent to her aunt's house to live. After being there for six months, her aunt died of heart disease, and Ingrid was sent to another aunt's home to live. During her first marriage, she had a daughter named Pia Lindstrom. Shortly after that, Ingrid left her husband with the baby behind to work in theater and film in the United States. Two years later, her husband and her daughter came to the States. Because she was working in California, and her daughter and her husband lived in New York, they didn't spend much time together. During this time, she wrote a letter to the director Roberto Rossellini, stating that she would like to work for him, which led to their affair. Hollywood's darling went from purity and goodness to the rebellious homewrecker, which strained her career in America.

When Ingrid became pregnant, she and Roberto sought divorces from their spouses and got married.

When our parents or parents die, we naturally become disconnected from *loving* someone or letting them be close to us, out of self-protection. Our inner child would say, "If I *love* you, you may leave me or die." And that is more than a child can take. It's also why some of us have lost a parent's *love* so freely and openly, because we know what it's like to lose a parent, and how precious time really is. *Love* is just a reflection of our own healing journey.

Diahann Carroll:

According to *Wikipedia*, Diahann Carroll was a child actor involved in the arts and entertainment industry and was modeling for *Ebony* magazine at age 15. She quit college to pursue an acting and modeling career. She was married four times, and during one of her marriages, she had an affair for nine years with Sidney Poitier, who tried to convince her to get a divorce, promising to do the same. Eventually, he did divorce, but he wanted to live with Diahann, but without her daughter, for six months -- to see if it would work out. Diahann refused.

In her book *The Legs are the Last to Go*, she talks about the traumatic event where her parents left her with her aunt in North Carolina for a year so they could get ahead back in New York. At the time, she was just a toddler; one day, she woke up at her aunt's house and there was no mother. Bewildered, she thought, "Why should my mother leave me without telling me why?" During this time with her aunt, Diahann would "fly into tantrums. My mother and father knew what they had to do to get ahead. But that one year without the security of my parents has stayed with me all these years." During this time, no one would answer her questions about her mother's whereabouts.

When she was reunited with her parents, they never discussed the "lost year," and her parents never discussed "difficult or disturbing incidents." Diahann, who felt "scarred by it," was left with a "deep feeling of abandonment." She felt that traumatic year contributed to her feeling of abandonment, and would make her attract the wrong type of men. For years, she felt that she had done something wrong to deserve the separation from her doting parents.

She had grown up with the image that her parents were "King and Queen;" she herself was doted on like a little princess. When she went to elementary school, she got a role in a play and became fixated on her performance. She worked hard to remember her lines, with her mother's encouragement. Her mother became fixated and motivated to encourage her daughter's newfound hobby and told her to take classes in piano and choir. She would oversee Diahann's costumes and dress, and make sure her daughter was clean, pretty, and respectable. In fact, her mother became involved in every aspect of the process; in return, her daughter wanted nothing more but to make her happy. One of her friends asked Diahann, "When are you going to give up that story?" She replied, "It's hard to give up the story." She was married four times, was never comfortable living alone, and looked to others to make her happy.

When she was with Sidney, he asked her to live with him, but without her daughter. The separation would have been a repeat of her separation from her parents as a child. Being cut off from that physical and emotional nourishment that only a mother can provide to a small child can have lasting effects, increasing the risks for relationships struggles with intimate partners, anxiety, and breast cancer. Diahann struggled with her relationships with men and was married four times and had an affair. The trauma that she endured as a toddler away from her parents would have contributed to her fear of abandonment and the broken connection to her mother could have contributed to her formation of breast cancer.

Hoda Kotb:

In her book, *Hoda: How I Survived War Zones, Bad Hair, Cancer, and Kathie Lee,* Hoda tells how her parents immigrated from Egypt to the U.S. when she was nine years old. As a child, she and her mother, brother, and sister took a trip back to Egypt, then had to evacuate due to bombing raids. That ended up being a 700-mile journey to safety. When she was in the 5th grade, her parents transferred to Nigeria for her father's work. She and her younger brother attended the same school, and she would listen for him to "cry out" because she had witnessed a teacher hit a student. This shocked her. When she went to her parents to tell them what had happened, they dismissed her story.

The following year, her family returned to the U.S., and then moved again to Virginia. It was hard for Hoda to assimilate into the U.S.; she was constantly explaining where she was from, how to say her name, and why she looked different. She was caught between three cultures: Egyptian, white, and African American. Her parents were very strict about curfews and dating. Eventually, when she went back to Egypt, Hoda was so culturally removed, she no longer fit in. Her father was not an emotional man, and because she was the middle child, she felt that she had to work twice as hard as the others. As a result, she kept her feelings bottled up inside.

When she was in college, her father died from a heart attack. She would later discover that her father experienced discrimination as well, but never told his family.

As her career started to take off, she found herself working in war zones all over the world, and even had to attend a camp for war zone situations. This would be the reenactment of the experience she and her family went through during her trip to Egypt as a child.

When children are constantly uprooted, they have a hard time feeling grounded and always feel out of place. Anyone who experiences fighting and war will probably have a traumatic response; in many people, you cannot see the trauma, but it's there. Our parents are there to keep us safe and protected, and sometimes there are unavoidable situations that our parents lead us into that affect us very deeply. Knowing what behaviors to look for and habits that form after the trauma helps people heal and recover.

Brigitte Bardot:

According to *Wikipedia*: Brigitte Bardot was born in France to a wealthy family; her father was a strict totalitarian parent who demanded that Brigitte and her sister have strict behaviors, table manners, and dress. Her mother chose whom Brigitte could associate with, and as a result, she had very few friends. During her childhood, she and her sister were playing in the house when they broke a vase;

her father whipped her sister, then referred to them as if they were "strangers." When she fell in *love* with her first husband as a teenager, her parents promptly bought her a train ticket to England for school, and she was so upset by this, she put her head into an oven that had an open flame. (Heart joy/love) Finally, her parents consented to the marriage when she was 18. As an adult, she had numerous affairs. When she had her son, he was raised by his father and his family, and only had a relationship with his mother after he was an adult. She also suffered from a nervous breakdown and suicide attempts.

In an article for vogue.fr, written by Olivier Lalanne and dated August 10, 2015, called *An Audience with Brigitte Bardot:* "Did you go into films for *love*?" B.B. (Brigitte Bardot) said, "No, that was to get the hell away from my parents. To earn my independence. And before becoming famous, I made some really trashy films. But they got me away from home and helped me to discover something that looked like freedom. It was all the more exciting because I had had a very strict upbringing. Going into films was an act of self-liberation." "Françoise Sagan once said, 'Brigitte *loves* found men and stray dogs who put their heads on her shoulder.' What do you say to that?" B.B.: "It's very pretty. And very thoughtful." O.L.: "Are you afraid of loneliness?" B.B.: "I used to be terrified of it. I couldn't stand it. I felt lost, abandoned, ready to do the stupidest things." When he asked her about her photos, "What do you feel when you see those images?" B.B.: "I never look at them. I don't want to dwell on the past. And if by chance I do see one, I think, 'Hey, she's pretty,' whereas back then, I thought I was ugly. Absolutely mad. I used to try and make myself as pretty as I could, and even like that, I still thought I was ugly. It was really hard to go out, to show myself. I was afraid of not coming up to people's expectations."

In an article written for guardian.com from the archive, September 24, 1996: *Brigitte Bardot Bares Her Soul* by Paul Webster, stated, "She neglected her only child, Nicholas, by the actor Jacques Charrier, and describes pregnancy as 'the punishment of God.'"

First leaks of her book "allude to alcohol abuse, self-destructive depression and a cinematic form of nymphomania in which the actress falls in *love* with her leading men from the first screen embrace.... 'When you live such intense moments as I have done, there is always a bill to pay,'-- she said, revealing that just before she retired at night, she drank two bottles of champagne and three bottles of wine a day." (Alcohol is processed in the liver, and liver is related to the emotion anger in TCM). "She has deliberately destroyed her image as a sex symbol by refusing cosmetic surgery, dressing badly, and, after giving away her Saint Tropez villa to her foundation, living in a small house surrounded by rescued animals, a rusty Renault 4L, and a broken-down Range Rover." Her rescued animals are her form of safe, non-judgmental, unconditional *love*.

"You mustn't think I am dissatisfied," she said. "That would be a form of bitterness. My life is now what I always wanted - what I dreamed about subconsciously." In public, she was preyed upon and constantly hounded everywhere she was, even in her own home.

On the bardotbrigitte.com website, she said: "I did not want to give birth to an additional human being. I think there are too many on Earth. And they scare me." Only the father wanted the child. She could not feel the *love* or instinct for parenting -- only for animals.

"At the time, the words used to describe her pregnancy were very hard: 'It was like a tumor that had nourished me, that I had carried in my swollen flesh, thinking only of the blessed moment in which I would finally rid it. The nightmare having reached its climax, I had to live, for life, the object of my misfortune.' "This sinister day, Brigitte Bardot gave birth, without painkillers, in a clinic of the 16th arrondissement of Paris. The pain was intense: 'Animal wounded to death, I screamed without restraint.'"

She stated in her book, *Brigitte Bardot: Initiales B.B.*: "When she was introduced to her child, she rejected it: 'I drive crazy; I did not want to see it anymore.'"

Her animal rescue reflected her own rescue, which never happened. As a child, her mother didn't stand up and protect her from her father's cruelty. This would explain her disconnection from her son, as well as her troubled and abusive relationships with men. The stress of living in the "box" can be an unbearable strain to any child. Wanting to "please" your parents in any way for fear of being abandoned or denied *love* is a horrible stress on any child.

In addition to her breast cancer, Bardot also had hip issues. The hips are located in the Root Chakra, which is feeling grounded or rooted in her life, as well as anxiety, depression and insecurity issues. The bones correlate to the kidney in TCM, which is related to fear and sexual issues.

After 57 years, she finally has a relationship with her son and grandchildren.

Linda McCartney:

An online article called *Linda McCartney: The Biography,* by Danny Fields from wingspan.ru, talked about Linda's parents. Her father was a prominent lawyer and of the Jewish faith; he was not comfortable with the uprising of anti-Semitism, so he decided to change his name from Epstein to Eastman. Her mother was from a prominent Jewish family in Chicago, who was very active in the community and her religion. Her parents were very active socially, and her mother, who was a wonderful hostess, made sure all her guests were well-fed and comfortable. On the other hand, Linda was not interested in socializing, and spent most of her time in the kitchen with the help during these social gatherings. She was an avid outdoors woman, spending much of her time with her brother John in the woods, scaring their parents when they were frequently out past dark. Her main interest was riding horses, and she spent hours acquiring many awards for her abilities. Linda was so quiet, no one in her school even knew of her accomplishments. School and studying didn't interest her, so she went to college in Arizona, far away from her home in New York; there, she could spend more time riding horses versus school.

She wanted to pursue a career in the arts, as a photographer. However, her father objected, and she had been considered the "black sheep" for this reason, according to Famouspeople.com.

Her parents had made a pact never to travel together for air travel, and yet when Linda was 21, her mother died in a plane crash. "I had never really connected with my mother," Linda told Zoe Heller for an article that appeared in *Vanity Fair* in October 1992 called *Moll of Kintyre.* "But for my father, it was a disaster. My parents had been very much in *love*. When Kooning wrote to my father after the death, he described the relationship as a 25-year *love* affair." Linda left school and returned home. "Her family was shattered..." Her younger sisters were 12 and 15 years old at the time of their mother's death, but instead of staying to help her family, Linda returned to Arizona and her boyfriend. "It was a kind of escapism." she told Heller, "I was very immature. I just escaped." Distraught upon her return, "she became pregnant within weeks of her return and married." Two years later, they separated.

One year after her mother's death, her father remarried to a woman with three sons, and Linda returned home with her daughter. She got a job at *Town & Country* magazine, where she got her break in photography, and proved that she could handle the moody artists and musicians she was photographing. When she met Paul McCartney initially, Linda felt that she wasn't special enough for such a famous and social celebrity; but when they got married, she was already pregnant. Linda's daughter Stella was born by C-section; her son James had a near-scare when he was surfing and was swept out to sea. She and her children followed Paul around the world and had many adventures.

When she was diagnosed with breast cancer, she didn't let anyone know. Her cancer ended up spreading into her liver, which is connected to the emotion anger in TCM. Her marriage to Paul, the outgoing public figure, may have been a repeat pattern of living with her outgoing and super-social mother.

Susan Goodman Komen:

Susan's sister Nancy G. Brinker wrote a book called *Promise Me*. She mentions her family's history of service to others, which was deeply instilled into their mother. Her family helped many others during the Great Depression. Their maternal grandmother Fritizi, helped found the local Red Cross chapter, would rely heavily on her only child, their mother, when she was assisting others in need. She also dedicated her life to helping the local hospital and hospice.

Their maternal grandmother Fritizi was accidentally given a lethal dose of sulfanilamide, while their mother watched her mother reeling in pain until her death. As a result, their mother was "fearless about questioning judgments of God, and doctors who think they were God's golf buddies."

When Susan was ten years old, the polio scare occurred. In 1953, parents were warned not to let their children swim in a pool, or be out and about, because of the poliovirus. During the scare, the town closed down, and she describes how her mother told her and Susan: "Dr. Moffett says children can get polio from going in the water." Nancy replied, "Clean water right out of the hose? How would that give a kid polio?" Their mother didn't know how the children were getting the virus, but she knew it was very contagious and so she was not taking any chances. Nancy balled herself up into a fetal position. Saddened at the thought of the many children who would be affected by this horrible virus, Nancy had envisioned crippled children in braces and wheelchairs. When she heard of another child in the neighborhood getting the virus, "It terrified her and broke her heart."

During this time, the girls had to accompany their mother on her own personal crusade to stamp out polio; she worked tirelessly, with her girls in tow. The sisters were doing their best to follow along with their mom, but girls being girls, they soon grew tired. One time when their mom was driving, the girls were carrying on in the back seat. This aggravated their mother and she pulled over and told the girls to "get out!" During this episode, their mother admonished them, "People have died for this country. People have sacrificed their lives so you could live in peace and freedom, and all that I ask of you is that you take care of it... You care enough about your community to look after those who aren't as fortunate as you." All the while, she was shaking her finger angrily at the girls. The only thing they could do was stare down at their shoes, avoiding eye contact with their mother, who would not let them back in the car until they both promised to be good "stewards." This guilt and shame motivated Susan to come up with the idea of putting on a variety show.

"Fritzi," Susan's maternal grandmother, her family "took in soldiers, tended the wounded, and comforted the dying during World War I" As a teenager, Fritzi and her sister Rose tended to their sister Esther, who was "disoriented and complaining of a strangely piercing headache." A doctor was summoned and "dashed water on her face, telling her frantic family, "She'll get up." Ninety minutes later, Esther was dead."

Susan's Aunt Rose had also suffered from breast cancer and had a mastectomy. Rose had witnessed her own sister's death as a teenager. Both Susan and her sister Nancy had a history of benign breast lumps. This horrible experience with the polio scare must have lingered in the back of her mind; it was as if her sister was doing her best to stamp out breast cancer, just as women all over the U.S. were doing their best to stamp out polio.

This is an example of how children's mirroring neurons kick in. The neurons allow us to assimilate into our caregiver's behavior, so we don't get abandoned. We fall into this pattern, thinking that if I do what they want, they will *love* me, and I won't be abandoned. Unfortunately, many of us spend a lifetime pleasing others rather than finding the love within ourselves.

Susan's cancer had now spread to the lymph nodes in her armpit. This is where the Heart meridian, which is related to the emotion joy/love, begins; and also travels through the lung, which is related to the emotions grief and sadness in TCM.

Just as humans get breast lumps, chickens get a disease called "Wooden Breast Syndrome," making the breast meat tough and chewy, and it's almost impossible to detect. This happens because the bird cannot metabolize fat correctly. Remember, you only eat female chicken, and female chicken breast tissue, and female hormones in that tissue. This may be a contributing factor to breast lumps. In addition, these birds have elevated levels of lipoprotein lipase, which is also found in breast cancers.

A website called, yourhormones.info describes: "Oestradiol is a steroid hormone made from cholesterol and is the strongest of the three naturally produced oestrogens. It is the main oestrogen found in women, and has many functions, although it mainly acts to mature and maintain the female reproductive system. For example, a natural increase in blood oestradiol concentrations during the menstrual cycle causes an egg to mature and be released; that is, to be ovulated. Another important role of oestradiol is thickening the lining of the uterus so that the egg can be implanted if it becomes fertilized. Oestradiol also promotes the development of breast tissue and increases both bone and cartilage density." **Estradiol, or oestradiol, is an estrogen steroid hormone.

There are two sources for cholesterol: One is its production in the liver, and the other is from animal products in our diet. Too much oestradiol, which is produced from cholesterol, can increase the risk of the formation of breast cancer. These hormones have a natural role in a person's body, but when we ingest animal products, the DNA, proteins, fats, and hormones are not compatible with ours, which causes confusion in the cells. This confusion leads our bodies to store these cells as "self" and will naturally find and package them for removal; this is what we call "cancer."

CHAPTER 18

Reconnection and Understanding Illnesses

Illnesses:

The beauty of any illness is that it's just a mirror of what we are struggling with emotionally. No matter how grave the situation may seem, remarkable turnarounds are possible. All diseases contain the deepest, darkest unresolved emotional secret that is there for you to discover, if you choose, not as a punishment, but as a mirror into which one can reflect. People have spent most of their lives fighting their authentic selves, trying to fit into someone else's life, attempting to abandon themselves and the intimate love that lies deep with us.

There will be no greater love in your life than what you give yourself. The question is, are you willing to take steps to discover what you're hiding? This question will never go away, usually found in a place shrouded in guilt, shame, abandonment, and humiliation. The person involved has been shackled all these years. I can promise you that you will feel nurtured, loved, and liberated if you allow this process to happen. I have seen the most astounding turnarounds happen, all there for the taking. The world is truly your oyster if you choose to do this!

As our inner child struggles, our adult self-abandons them, cutting off all forms of communication and acknowledgment. In the process, we fail to see our connection to our higher self. If you watch a parent suddenly abandon a child, it's shocking and disheartening to see that child struggle. We do the same to our own inner child. This disconnection or denial is also part of both PTSD, and the self-preservation of the unhealthy pattern. When you observe someone struggling with a health issue, you will see the inner child pop out. The illness or disease will only be a reflection of their unresolved emotional trauma. The person will act like a needy child who wants so badly to be *loved* and *nurtured*. They can become as needy and helpless as newborns. Their diet may become more child-like: soft foods, or comfort foods. Some even have to be spoon-fed. This allows them to revert back to the mother-child bond, where they are dependent on another to take care of them.

So many people talk about their spouses, who weren't there for them emotionally, especially when they needed them the most. The reality is that we have long abandoned ourselves, and that the ones we attract are only a reflection of what we need to heal from in our past. **The universe will make us repeat this cycle until we choose to acknowledge, learn and heal.**

Reconnection:

There are many ways to disconnect in our society -- cell phones, headphones, computers, a million channels on TV. We as a society need to start to reconnect. Start first with yourself, in a loving and supportive way: add in meditation, healthy cooking, creative writing, hypnosis, yoga, reiki, reflexology, acupuncture, music therapy, or just being with nature into your new lifestyle.

Remember when you first moved away from home? You wanted to truly know and appreciate your new space, so you became familiar with all its nooks and crannies. Your mind, body, and spirit are where you live. So explore and understand why your body speaks to you in its unique way. Ask yourself: Do you and your body seem loving, nurturing, and supportive, or has your body been screaming at you? And *how* and, most especially, *why* haven't you been paying attention? **More importantly, why wouldn't you?** These steps are imperative for a long, healthy, and peaceful life.

Be that old sage who dies in their sleep. It's easy to put off what you can do the next day, and you can get easily get distracted. But...**You would never think about putting off breathing until tomorrow, would you?** Think about how amazing your life will be when you dedicate your life to yourself! If you wait, you'll be at the doctor's office, or worse, in the hospital, hoping and praying that the illness will somehow magically go away. What you're really doing is hoping that your hurting parts that you haven't ever worked on or acknowledged will magically disappear. That's like asking your thumbs to disappear, although you use them every day.

How many times have you or your friends gone to doctors, psychologists, psychics, or tarot card readers to find the answers to the questions that already lie within you? **It's like hiding the pot of gold from yourself. Why on earth would you do that?** The reality is that we have already survived the traumatic events we have stuffed. Now it's time to begin talking or thinking about them. This is what we must face in order to heal. I am reminded of the Quest for the Holy Grail, that beautiful cup that nourishes and quenches our body, mind, and spirit. It's always available to you if you want it, so what - or, who? -- is stopping you? Fear, anger, grief, sadness, abandonment, shame, and guilt are emotions that keep you a prisoner, unable to be your true, authentic self. On the other hand, compassion, love, joy, and gratitude fill a cup from which you can drink anytime, if you choose to do so.

It's Time to Talk:

That sweet child inside you needs your close attention, just as they did as a little child, when they wanted mommy to protect them. It's time to ask your inner child some very important questions; and the only way you can do this is from their perspective. It's a big deal to your inner child that you understand them at their level, just as you wanted mommy to do so long ago. So, grab craft paper you color on, and a crayon, to get you into your inner child's head. Then ask your inner child these questions to help open up communication.

Why did mommy do__________________________?

Why couldn't she__________________________?

I needed her when_________________________?

Why didn't she tell me________________________?

Why didn't she stay_________________________?

Why didn't mommy ask_______________________?

How could mommy not know___________________?

Why wasn't mommy there for me when____________?

Why does mommy make me____________________?

Why does mommy like them better______________?

Why doesn't mommy help me__________________?

Why did mommy need________________________?

*** There are no right or wrong answers to these questions. You can answer them as many times as you need to, in order to keep an open conversation going. However, your inner child needs you now more than ever. You can always interchange the name mommy with your name and answer the questions from your adult self.

Why did I do_______________________?

Why couldn't I_______________________?

I need me when_______________________?

Why didn't I tell myself_______________________?

Why did I stay_______________________?

Why didn't I ask_______________________?

How could I have not known_______________________?

Why wasn't I there for myself when_______________________?

Why did I make myself_______________________?

Why do I like them better than myself_______________________?

Why don't I help myself when_______________________?

CHAPTER 19

Self-Abandonment

A Bit About Love:

Remember 1 Corinthians 13?

"Love is patient, love is kind. It does not envy; it does not boast; it is not proud. It does not dishonor others. IT IS NOT SELF-SEEKING."

Wait? What?

"Love is not self-seeking"......YES! Because you are made of love and light. You're already made of LOVE because you are a child of the universe, God, Buddha, Jesus. 96% of your body is made up of the four essential elements that are found in the universe: hydrogen (Water), carbon (Earth), nitrogen (Wood) and oxygen (Wind). As a human, you will always be self-seeking. We'll always think "what's in it for me" in every situation. But when we realize that all the love we could already want or need already exists within ourselves, then we will start to realize that no one, NO ONE will ever *love* us as much as we love ourselves. It's our universal God-given right as part of something so big and powerful that a source of pure, everlasting energy, love, and light is, as they say, already within us.

We only seek *love* and acceptance from others because the broken people who raised us who were so toxic, they could never teach us self-love. **Learning how to love oneself is the greatest human lesson we can learn.** Our parents or guardians couldn't see it through their own toxic shame, abandonment, and hurt that they had endured as children. As a result, many of us are walking wounded, enduring pain that we believe we deserve. I met an elderly person who was bent over, leaning on their cane in pain, crying, and saying, "I deserve the pain. I deserve the pain." When I asked, "What do you mean?" They told me, "I was one of several kids, and I wouldn't listen to my father, and so he beat me. I deserve the pain."

For every person in pain, I see the deep emotional element, usually from childhood, that has a grip on them so tight that they believe it is a permanent part of who they are. They cannot let go of these experiences. When this happens, you realize that as a friend, family member, or practitioner, you can do nothing to help them -- because they fully believe in their conscious mind that they deserve the pain. That unresolved trauma is what blocks many people from healing.

Fear

Fear is a trigger for the fight, flight, or freeze response, also known as PTSD. When we're children, it could be simply seeing or hearing a fire truck, or a police officer, or a look our mother or father give us. Or the experiences can be life-changing -- such as having surgery or witnessing someone who has an illness or is dying, or hearing our parents yell and scream at each other, or experiencing abuse. Because the brain has not fully formed, our reactions as infants and toddlers will be reactionary and primal. Even though I was never around my dad that much, I remember the look he would give me. I was very fearful of him, to the point where I have always been afraid of men, especially in uniform. I choose men who have abandonment issues, or ones with deep emotional trauma that reflects what I haven't yet worked on within myself.

Shame

Shame can drive us to incredible greatness or leave us in a state of great misery. Yet, it's a necessary component of our conscious mind. Everyone has experienced it, and we have been in its grips since before we can remember. Shame is what society has tried to use to control the population, family, friends, etc.

Shame is a self-conscious emotion; it's our way of wounding ourselves. Whether it be real or imagined, shame can make us believe that we're not worth it. That somehow, we've done something to deserve our self-entrapment. We begin to view ourselves only focusing on our imperfections and shortcomings. We fill ourselves with what we believe are legitimate reasons we can't be *loved*, successful, happy, etc. These toxic lessons have been handed down from our parents, because they've masked and projected their shame upon us. We do it, out of self-preservation, to others, either jokingly or as a way to control someone else's behavior. If we shame others, then we believe we have put value or power into our self-worth. This allows someone to control another in a relationship, and over time we believe this false dialogue as true because someone who *loves* us said it. If our parents, guardians, siblings shamed us because of their unresolved trauma, we'll seek it again because *the toxic pattern looks like love*. Shame is just an example of something that emotionally pops up so we can reflect and heal from this toxic pattern.

I had a friend who, every time I visited, I would get this overwhelming feeling that whatever I did, I was never going to be good enough or smart enough. Now, the person never made me feel this way, but it was still there. So, I asked myself, "Have I ever felt this way before?" The answer is "yes." See, this person was just a reminder to my consciousness that

I have work to do in this area of my life. They were a reflection of my childhood experiences from my own family, and once I recognized this, I was able to let go of the emotion. It's always important to thank your emotions. Be grateful for the emotional experience, because it is part of your human experience.

When we are young, we don't have the skill set or the authority to reply, so we can grow and heal. So instead, we take these blows that influence the course of our lives, and we spend most of our lives adapting to these new uncomfortable patterns. They can turn into an addiction, however, if they are not discovered and healed.

The difference between guilt and shame is that guilt is about an act or task, and shame is about how individuals view or feel about themselves. Therefore, shame can hinder personal relationships such as parent-child, teacher-student, doctor-patient, spouse, or partner. This affects the trust and security in the relationship.

Once someone feels shame, it will have a ripple effect on nearby people because they must alter their behavior to hide their own shame. Shame can inhibit our ability to express our emotions because we are in fear of damaging our reputation. When we start to experience shame, we turn inward, and begin to self-torment, be judgmental, not feel good about ourselves, stupid, or whatever, we want to self-punish. We begin to feel that our core belief is that we are fundamentally flawed and defective. In doing so, we will begin to isolate ourselves to protect ourselves from exposure to further shame. Shame can lie deep within our subconscious and can be unknown even to ourselves. As a result, we isolate, alienate, become workaholics, alcoholics, drug-addicted, or food-addicted. As we compensate for these stuck emotions, our bodies will also feel the impact, and we will choose some form of addiction to numb ourselves out, so we feel "normal" in order to self-regulate. As a result of having an addiction, the addict no longer has healthy boundaries, and so they lose the ability to say "no," which only increases their shame.

When we feel shamed by a person or parent who raised us, we secretly long for this relationship to heal, so we will no longer feel isolated and abandoned. This primitive drive is so strong, from the time we are babies to about 15 years old. We need these people to help us survive, and to establish a healthy sense of trust. When we live in a state of shame, we feel raw and exposed, and our primal fear of abandonment takes over, which changes our fundamental behavior. Shame can also keep us from trusting anyone, telling the truth, or enjoying life, as well as inhibiting our ability to heal.

Parenting with shame:

There are many ways parents or caregivers can unknowingly contribute to a child's shame. Shame-based parenting is used to control any behavior the parent or caregiver wants to stop, behavior they deem annoying or negative. This type of parenting also comes from a place of one-sided authority, in which the child has no say or control over the conversation. When the parent has their own unresolved issues, this may alter how they react to, or raise, the child. In many cases, parents may re-enact their own shame-based childhood. Here are some reasons behind shame-based parenting: Excessive work, feeling overwhelmed, self-judging, addictions, unresolved childhood traumas, physical issues or disabilities, harsh tones, or reactionary emotions. This may cause the parent or caregiver to: induce guilt in the child, spank, scold, punish, publicly humiliate, fat-shame, not let the child do things for themselves, have unrealistic expectations, ignore a child, name-call, etc.

Though we may be traveling on different roads, all roads lead to enlightenment.

CHAPTER 20

Healing Process

Healthy Family:

A healthy family unit has a deep sense of commitment to one another; they make time together a priority. This will look like open communication, where conversations are valued, and people are non-judgmental. Opinions and appreciation are often expressed, and participants look out for each other's well-being. Conflicts or differences of opinion are expressed and resolved --constructively and promptly.

This, in turn, allows the children to grow up in a healthy and safe environment where they feel safe, trusted, *loved,* and supported. As a result, they grow up to be resilient, independent, curious, creative, expressive, resourceful, empathetic.

A word about love:

Love has never been about pain. Love is about self-discovery, and all emotions are maps that help guide us to self-love. Emotions flow into our lives like a signpost of self-awareness, and give us directions to where we need to explore within ourselves. They help us discover areas within ourselves that were previously unseen, which help us find our self-love. These emotions and diseases, even cancer, are signposts saying, **"stop here and self-check." It's a journey that one must take in order to find oneself.**

No one wants the responsibility of taking care of you, and if they do, then it's their inner child trying to rescue their parent that they still struggle with, and they are longing for that *love*. So during your life's journey, you will find people who bring out emotions in you, and they are there only as a reflection to help you see your truth. But as they flow into your life and your journey, the majority won't stay, and that's OK. What you'll find pops up on this journey of self-discovery are all the things that show you the broken patterns, which our broken parents, guardians, siblings taught us. What we think is *love* is only self-preservation and self-struggle. **It's not love.**

Our parents lived in patterns of shame, guilt, and abandonment from their unresolved traumas, which helped them survive their childhood. It's these broken patterns of our ancestors and the people who raised us, and it's what we believe is *love*. It's the lie we tell ourselves to try and fit in with people we don't belong with, in order to repeat the broken patterns, we learned as children. We make numerous attempts at what we call *love* to rescue the reflection of some parent, sibling, or guardian who raised us while abandoning our own needs, wants, and desires. As we pour ourselves into another broken human being, trying to rescue them, we lose ourselves in the process, and we become sick, angry, addicted, and out of balance. This activates our emotional inner child, who becomes needy and childish, and all decisions, including what we eat, will center on what that little child wants to ease their pain. They'll always seek a fleeting pain/pleasure addiction cycle, and never happiness. The inner child struggles, fearing abandonment and the false form of *love* it believes is true. This is why there are so many death bed confessions, because the inner child feels safe that no more harm or abandonment will come to them.

Don't wait until it's too late. Make changes. Be honest with yourself and learn about what you love and what feels good and right. We all want that beautiful *love* story, and it starts with the person in the mirror, so being willing to forgive yourself is of the utmost priority. **Learn to fall in love with yourself**. We are worth that. Every one of us! It's the first step of self-discovery, a journey filled with many peaks and valleys, all blessings. Even though it may take some time to discover your truths, the journey is well worth it. As we shed these old patterns of pain, dysfunction, and false love, we become strong, independent and knowledgeable about who we truly are. Most of all, take your time and keep asking powerful questions to get to the answers.

Isn't that what our healthy parents or guardians (God, Supreme Being, Elohim, El, 'ilah, Qi, Om, Krishna, Bhagavad, Jesus, Buddha, Dalai Lama, angels, spirit guides ....) would want for us?

Above all: It's OK to forgive.

Honor people's journeys. They are based on their individual struggles, which have nothing to do with you. Encourage them to continue on their journey and wish them well.

CHAPTER 21

Components of the Mother-Child Bond

Healthy Mother:

To look into therapies for healing, we have to revert to the healing bond between mother and child. A healthy mother/child bond combines many therapies to produce cohesive healing, leaving the child feeling safe, nourished, loved, and nurtured. This allows the child's brain to release chemicals and hormones to let the child know that everything is OK. This emotional and physical reset will be needed in some fashion for the rest of our lives. Mother's original therapy includes her voice, touch, nourishment, and a healthy environment for the infant to survive in and thrive.

Mother's Voice:

She's the first person we hear long before we are born, and while we're swimming around in her nice warm tummy for almost ten months, her voice activates our brain. A baby always feels soothed, safe, warm, and nurtured when they hear mommy's voice. In the *Stanford Medical News* dated May 16, 2016, an article written by Erin Digitale called, *Mom's Voice Activates Many Different Regions in Children's Brains,* says, "Brain regions that respond more strongly to the mother's voice extend beyond auditory areas to include those involved in emotion and reward processing, social functions, detection of what is personally relevant and face recognition.…Many of our social, language and emotional processes are learned by listening to our mom's voice." This means mothers' actions have a significant impact on how we interact with ourselves and others. She is the first person who provides us with emotional comfort.

In an online article by Beata Mostafavi, on August 15, 2019, from labblog.uofmhealth.org titled, *Mom's Voice May Help Babies Sleep Better in the NICU,* babies were played a recording of their mom's voices reading books. The babies slept better and woke up less frequently. "What we found was that, during the times when noise levels were high, babies were more likely to stay asleep when the recording of their mothers' voices played." Also, "When babies are first born, they respond preferentially to their mother's voice and their mother's native language. presumably because that's what they're exposed to in the womb." Mother's voice is an essential part of the baby getting reassurance so they can sleep peacefully, which is necessary for healthy brain function.

Mother's Touch:

From the moment a baby is born, skin-to-skin contact is essential, because it allows the baby to continue with the familiar connection with mother that the baby had in utero. The baby can feel the mother's skin, temperature, heartbeat, voice, and touch, which will be the most familiar environment in order to adjust to this new environment. From an online article for *psychcentral.com* dated April 3, 2020, *Skin-to-Skin Touch Boosts Baby's Brain Development,* by Janice Wood: Researchers have discovered during a six-week skin-to-skin contact with the mother that infants had higher "cognitive and emotional regulatory skills" using the Kangaroo Care method. "Our findings across several studies demonstrate a link between the supportive dimensions of maternal caregiving behavior and left-hemisphere neurodevelopment, with maternal warmth and sensitivity predicting greater regulatory abilities and secure attachment," said Nancy Aaron Jones, PhD, senior author, an associate professor, director of the FAU WAVES Emotion Laboratory in the Department of Psychology, and member of the FAU Brain Institute (I-BRAIN). "Full-term infants and their mothers' likely benefit from the positive interactive experiences inherent in extended

Kangaroo Care use." Study co-authors are Jillian S. Hardin, Ph.D., who conducted the study for her dissertation; Krystal D. Mize, Ph.D., and Melanie Platt, Ph.D., all with FAU's Charles E. Schmidt College of Science.

In an online article from washington.edu/news dated January 16, 2018, titled: *A 'Touching Sight': How Babies' Brains Process Touch Builds Foundations for Learning,* by Kim Eckart: "Touch is the first of the five senses to develop…Long before babies acquire spoken language, touch is a crucial channel of communication between caregivers and babies….. The evidence of activity in the somatosensory cortex for both 'felt touch' and 'observed touch' show that 7-month-old infants have already made a basic connection between 'self' and 'other,' which researchers say lays the groundwork for imitating and learning from the behavior of other people, and for empathizing with them." The article discussed how the baby's brain is activated with physical touch and observation of touch, such as mom and dad touching each other.

According to the website caringforkids.cps.ca, in the article, *Your Baby's Brain: How Parents Can Support Healthy Development,* "Your baby's brain wiring is not fully connected at birth. It is very active, changing, and developing in response to what's going on all around them. It is the day-to-day experiences-

-activities like playing, being read to, learning, interacting and being responded to by people-that helps to develop your baby's brain.... Relationships are crucial. *Loving,* consistent, positive relationships help build healthy brains and protect your baby's brain from the negative effects of stress. Even young infants can experience stress when the places they live and play in feel unsafe, or are frightening. 'toxic' stress, which is much more serious than short-lived, everyday stress, is caused by persistent problems like extreme marital conflict, poverty, abuse, neglect, being exposed to violence, having a parent who abuses drugs or alcohol, or has an untreated mental illness. Toxic stress is harmful to your baby's developing brain. It can lead to physical, learning and emotional problems in childhood, and these problems can carry on right into adulthood."

An online article from digest.bps.org.uk titled *Neuro Harlow: The Effect of a Mother's Touch on Her Child's Developing Brain,* written by Christian Jarrett, talked about how touch plays a vital role in developing a social brain. "In the 1950s, the American psychologist Harry Harlow famously showed that infant rhesus monkeys would rather cling to a surrogate wire mother covered in cozy cloth, than to one that provided milk. A loving touch is more important even than food, the findings seemed to show. Around the same time, the British psychoanalyst John Bowlby documented how human children deprived of motherly contact often go on to develop psychological problems. Now, this line of research has entered the neuroscience era, with a study in *Cerebral Cortex* claiming that children with more tactile mothers tend to have more developed social brains."

The more a mother touches a child, the more the child will touch the mother, and this behavior is essential for developing healthy social skills. Wow! It's a wonder any of us come out unscathed! Since the mother-child bond is so strong, it would make sense why so many people seek out sexual relationships, possibly re-enacting the mother-child bond through touch, tone, skin-to-skin contact, and the closeness of the one-on-one relationship. In addition, there might be a subconscious reason why some people like to suckle, possibly re-enacting the primal nourishment or oral fixation.

CHAPTER 22

Acknowledging the Patterns

Withholding *Love*:

We all go through a lot in our childhood; whether the moments are big and traumatic or small episodes will impact our lives. Everyone carries these childhood burdens, even our parents, and they do the best job they can with what information they have gathered through their own traumatic experiences. **There is no right or wrong. There just is**. The sooner we allow ourselves to see and understand the truth, the sooner we can forgive ourselves, as well as our broken parents. In turn, this will allow for our healing. However bad it may be, the truth will not change, but we *can* change our viewpoint. During our flawed childhood, many of us learn conditional *love* or how to withhold *love*. Many people say, "*Love* hurts." "You broke my heart." "I tried to *love* you." The reality is that we haven't learned to love ourselves. We negative-self-talk or blame others for how they made us feel, but the truth of the statement is that **we are doing it to ourselves** as adults. Breaking this cycle is an essential step to healing. So many times, I hear people bashing men or bashing women, only in an attempt to justify their behavior and let themselves off the hook.

It's time to change your internal dialogue. Think of negativity as ignorance, and there is no room for negativity in healing, only **love, compassion, and understanding.** You're the only one who knows what you need and want in your life to heal, so don't be the one to hold back from yourself.

Remember the Bible, 1 Corinthians 13: "Love is patient, love is kind. It does not envy; it does not boast; it is not proud. It does not dishonor others; **it is not self-seeking."** Hmm....Then why is it that we spend a lifetime chasing this paper tiger? We forget that we've already been created in **LOVE.** So yeah, stop chasing and start looking in the mirror,' cause that person staring back at you needs all the love that you can possibly give, so start pouring that love back into yourself. You can't possibly give something to someone else that you deny to yourself........**LOVE.**

Abandonment

The common thread among all these people is that they have experienced a form of abandonment, whether it's physical or emotional. They are left with some form of an empty hole, which leads them into a life of searching for that one person or thing to fill that hole, all the while abandoning themselves. There are many forms of abandonment that children are faced with, such as the birth of a sibling, death, addiction, mental illness or illnesses, divorce, working parents, or parents that struggle with their own childhood traumas. Whatever reason these patterns occur when we're children, they become ingrained into our pattern of behavior as adults. As a result, we pick relationships or situations that mimic the abandonment behavior we were exposed to as children. This unhealthy pattern leads to cheating, abuse, weight issues, death, lack of intimacy, depression, addiction or workaholic, and harmful patterns of self-abuse. These patterns will reinforce the reason for someone to abandon us all over again, and we become desperate for someone to *love* us, and we will do anything to fit in to avoid re-abandonment.

As children, we want to be *loved*, nurtured, and accepted by our parents. It's nature's strong mother-child bond that keeps us alive and is at our core existence. We want to be valued by others and we need companionship to help ensure our survival. This primal nurturing sets the tone for the rest of our lives, feeling safe enough for us to grow, trust, and be independent. Yet, even in a healthy relationship, there can be periods when we feel the fear of abandonment. This activates our primal brain, causing a reaction of resentment, anger, emotional outburst, neediness, childlike reactions, blaming, closing down communication or lack of intimacy, and creating illnesses.

As resentment festers, we will find behaviors to compensate for the lack of closeness in others and we will abandon ourselves in the process. This self-betrayal will cause an equal and unwanted behavior that will lead us down a path to self-destruction. Cancer is the ultimate form of self-abuse and self-abandonment, which has been created out of feelings of resentment because we relied on someone or something other than ourselves to fill our own needs. Self-punishment, self-betrayal, and self-sabotage occur because our brains have become programmed by the mother-child bond for survival. As adults, we become re-abandoned and childlike all over again when we revert to our original patterns of behavior as a survivor mechanism.

I have witnessed this repeatedly in adults who will do anything for their parents, spouses, children, or significant people in their lives. In the process of making sure they don't abandon these toxic people, they sacrifice their own lives, trying to save someone else. Why do you think people become so connected to their animals? Because they have fewer chances of an animal abandoning them.

The reality is that we can only indeed abandon ourselves, and people can only meet you where they're at in their lives......

It's a sad thing to watch someone with cancer struggle with such deep-rooted issues as abandonment. This is intertwined with guilt and shame, even though they fail in many cases to recognize that it even exists. We must support our journey first and be selfless in our own nurturing, rather than rescuing someone else who has no intention of saving themselves. **"Actions speak louder than words."** So it's essential to start with ourselves, first and foremost, and do what feels good, loving, and nurturing. Do what feels safe and healthy, leaving you with no regrets at the end of the day, only gratitude. Remember that there's a higher power in this vast universe that's guiding and nurturing us every step of the way, toward a positive healing direction, so find your faith in that knowing. **Look around you every day, see all the miracles around you, and view life with the wonderment of a child. Be grateful for both the good and the bad, and realize that all of it teaches you how to go forward on your healthy healing journey. Always trust that.**

We are so used to our mothers or our children filling our gaps that we fail to learn how to fill them ourselves, leading us to our greatest abandonment. If we fail to see the pattern, we will constantly search for someone or something to fill it, some sort of distraction from ourselves. Well, if mommy could do it...... It's something very pronounced in adoptees and birth moms, but I think it's less common to talk about with people who are still with their families. We all have our life burdens, and none of us come out unscathed, but are we willing to heal? Or does our inner child tell us that we're not worthy of being in a loving relationship with ourselves and so we must seek out someone to fix us? Who are we really? Can we find happiness within ourselves? All these answers lie within us. Think about your lifelong characteristics or struggles, and who exactly you are mimicking.... Mommy, daddy, grandparents, siblings, cousins.... Think about how vital it is for us to fit in as children to survive. Can we recognize and break these cycles as adults? If we become aware of the pattern of behavior and recognize it when it happens, we can explore how we feel. A habit takes about 88 days to break. Can you do something different for 88 days, using multiple approaches, in order to lead a new and fulfilling life?

I don't think we need to repeat history, though it seems that society itself does this all the time. You can see that the pattern of addiction and survival happens on a mass scale, but can you do something each day to make a healthier difference in your own life?

CHAPTER 23

Buddha's Discoveries

Buddhism's 4 truths

As the story goes, Buddha was born to a Queen in India, and seven days after his birth, his mother died. His father, the King, sheltered him from the outside world, grooming him to be the future King, and so he lived a life of luxury and pleasure. However, even though Buddha grew up in this life, there was an emptiness in his heart, and one day he asked to be taken out to the countryside for the first time in his life. On his first trip outside the palace, he saw an old man and learned that he himself would become old; on his second trip, he saw a man suffering from an illness and learned he too would become sick. On his third trip, he discovered a man dying, and he learned too that this was his fate, and on his fourth trip, there lay a dead man. He discovered that this too was his fate.

These are lessons Buddha learned that would become the Four Sights.

On his trips, I like to say that Buddha learned the meaning of the word "foresight," for he now knew what his future held, but what could he do about it? He set out to learn about these human truths. Along his quest, Buddha sought the knowledge of the greatest teachers, and through this journey, he endured great suffering of his own affliction in an attempt to understand the meaning of human life and enlightenment. Although he experienced these great hardships, they never seemed to bring him closer to ending suffering or finding enlightenment or God. Only when he sat down to meditate (pray) did he discover that this was the only way to achieve his awakening (be close to God and internal peace). This allowed him to discover the *Four Noble Truths, Five Spiritual Faculties,* and their interconnection to the *Sensory Faculties.*

The Five Spiritual Faculties:

Faith/Belief

Energy/Persistence

Mindfulness/Memory

Stillness of the Mind

Wisdom/Understanding

Mindfulness encompasses all the Spiritual Faculties.

These are interconnected with the **6 Sensory Faculties.**

Vision: (Liver/gall bladder in TCM, and the emotions anger/frustration and worry)

Hearing: (Kidney/urinary bladder and the emotion fear)

Smell: There are five smells that are related to all the organs in TCM:

> **Water Element:** Kidney/urinary bladder and the smell of putrid(urine)or rotten.
>
> **Earth Element:** Spleen, stomach, pancreas and the smell of rotting apples.
>
> **Wood Element:** Liver/gall bladder and the smell of sour or acid.
>
> **Metal Element:** Lung, large intestine and the smell of rotten(fish) or rank.

Fire Element: Heart, small Intestine, san jiao, pericardium, and the smell of something scorched or burnt.

Taste:(Heart) There are five tastes that are related to all the organs in TCM.

Salty (kidney/bladder), sweet (spleen, stomach, pancreas), sour (liver, gall bladder), pungent (lung, large intestine), bitter (heart, small intestine, san jiao, pericardium)

Touch: (Lung - emotions of grief and sadness)

Thought: (Spleen/stomach/pancreas and the emotions of pensiveness or thoughtlessness)

In the magazine *Lion's Roar*, an article dated March 12, 2018, by Melvin Mcleod called *What are the Four Noble Truths?* said, "What are the four noble truths? Buddhism's famed four truths are called noble because they liberate us from suffering. Moreover, they are the Buddha's primary teaching, encapsulating the entire Buddhist path"

1. Suffering/Unsatisfactory

"Life always involves suffering in obvious and subtle forms. So even when things seem good, we always feel an undercurrent of anxiety and uncertainty inside."

2. The Cause of Suffering/Negative Desires

"The cause of suffering is craving and fundamental ignorance. We suffer because of our mistaken belief that we are a separate, independent, solid 'I.' The painful and futile struggle to maintain this delusion of ego is known as samsara, or cyclic existence."

3. The End of Suffering/End Negative Desires

"The good news is that our obscurations are temporary. They are like passing clouds that obscure the sun of our enlightened nature, which is always present. Therefore, suffering can end because our obscurations can be purified, and an awakened mind is always available to us."

4. The Path

"By living ethically, practicing meditation, and developing wisdom, we can take exactly the same journey to enlightenment and freedom from suffering that the Buddhas do. We, too, can wake up."

The Nobel Eightfold Path: Right understanding, right thought, right speech, right action, right livelihood, right effort, right mindfulness, right concentration.

> **"Monkey mind is actually a Buddhist term that refers to a mind that is restless, agitated, confused, or that is hard to control."**
> **- George Mumford—***The mindful Athlete: Secrets to Pure Performance*

"Yesterday I was so clever, so I wanted to change the world. Today I am wise, so I am changing myself."
- Rumi—Persian poet

"You are the community now. Be a lamp for yourselves. Be your own refuge. Seek no other. All things must pass. Strive on diligently. Don't give up."
- Buddha

Buddha stated that there are: *Wikipedia*

"Three poisons: Greed, anger, and ignorance

Three opposites: Generosity, compassion, and wisdom"

"Strong emotions are based on ignorance."
- Dalai Lama

We attack the negative image of a person that we create in our minds, not the person themselves. They are but a mere reflection of our own traumatized selves. These strong negative emotions are based on an illusion created in our minds to justify the reason for the feeling in the first place.

In Buddhism, negative emotions are based on ignorance.

CHAPTER 24

Discovering Self

Life is a process of self-discovery

To find treasure, one must be willing to dig deep in the sand or the ocean's depths, to risk all that is known, for the true treasures of the *soul*. It's at this great depth that we strip away the false narrative of our lives to discover the treasures of our *souls*, for it's there that our true wealth is found.

It's an adventure that should be taken every day. Even if you are afraid or feel awkward, go ahead and take the journey -- because we can never truly understand ourselves and heal if we continue to be afraid to reflect on how we came to be. We are a product of the circumstances and surroundings that we were brought up in, but they are never truly a reflection of ourselves. When we're children, we mirror to survive, and hopefully thrive, under the guidance of the people who raised us, but it's essential for us as little birds to leave the nest -- both emotionally and physically. I have seen so many people guilted into taking care of people who caused their original trauma, only to get sick as a result. I have seen adults fall apart when their parent, with whom they've had unresolved traumas, dies because their inner child hasn't healed. They've lived waiting for Mommy or Daddy to awaken and become the *loving* and nourishing parent they have always dreamed of. This can lead us into future relationships where we seek out someone who we can "fix" and "make us better" so they can *love* us the way we think we deserve, repeating the cycle of our inner child waiting for mommy and daddy to awaken from their trauma so they can *love* us.

How do we heal from all the crap we carry?

Research! Look at it all like a mad science experiment! Look for the patterns of behavior that are the result of a person's trauma. Take a look at family illnesses, for these are telltale signs of some kind of hidden trauma. Ask questions, even the uncomfortable ones, to your siblings and family members, and remember, your family is as "Sick as their secrets." Research anything and everything, so you can heal and look at your family's patterns of trauma and then release them. They are not you, and they're not love! We are perfectly flawed, and also perfectly capable of healing and understanding. **Remember: An acorn doesn't become a tree until it completely comes apart!**

Discover how to love yourself.

Learn acceptance of everything as it is, not what you wished it to be. Reclaim the person in the mirror and find what you love and admire about yourself, then do little things every day to nurture yourself, as only you can. Reclaim the best parts of your childhood, the little things that brought you joy: Warm pjs from the dryer in the winter, a bubble bath with ducks and toy boats, silly string, merry-go-rounds, swinging on a swing set, riding a bike, playing in the woods, making a fort, water balloons, squirt gun.... all the things that brought you silly joy and laughter, or comfort from your stressful days as a child. Incorporate those things back into your life, to help nurture and heal your child self. Don't ever forget that beautiful child within yourself! Your inner child will be with you for the rest of your life. There is always a lesson, and healing is the most liberating thing you will ever do. So give yourself that gift!

CHAPTER 25

Mood-Augmenters

How to raise dopamine and serotonin levels naturally

Every day, make choices to be a superhero-in-training, because this is a lifelong journey to healing and understanding, and being honest and happy with yourself. Each day do something to make the day epic: Make a call, write, sing, dance, meditate, learn, read, vision-board, paint, etc..... there are no rights or wrongs, and there is no self-judgment. Make it spontaneous and fun, and make it random. **You can even make your own superhero costume! Make it spectacular! Be a do-gooder to increase these feel-good hormones.**

When we live our lives in fear, anger, and frustration, and a what's-in-it-for-me attitude, these lower our feel-good chemicals...so don't get caught up in the crap vacuum! The more we focus on the outside world than ourselves, the more we become disconnected from ourselves, our wants and needs, and what feels good, healthy, and healing. We become enslaved to others -- trying to fill their bottomless pit of wants and desires. This needless distraction leaves you no time to focus on yourself. So ask yourself, **"Why in the world would you want to avoid yourself?"** The prize has never been about getting someone to *love* us. **The prize is learning how to love ourselves.** But we have created a life of endless tasks to avoid ourselves. Just think about how many times you have put off exercising or eating a healthy sit-down meal. Ask yourself: **"Why on earth wouldn't you want to love and nourish yourself? Who else is going to do it?"** Sometimes we cannot avoid our environment, but if we can change our perspective or point of view of it, then we can see it with fresh eyes -- as if it's something we've never seen before. Fresh eyes, thoughts, sounds, and a new creation can do wonders for any situation. Think about it this way: What if you were watching your favorite movie, and you realized for the very first time a phrase, person, or setting that you had never seen before. **New opportunities are everywhere, and when you open yourself up to them, they will appear and shed new light or a new direction, and in turn, change your point of view.**

We all face many stressful situations and with these occurrences, **we can either choose to be a victim or be a victor.** We could focus on the pain or the loss and seek the pleasure (cycle of addiction) or choose to see happiness, compassion, and understanding.

How many times have you stressed out about something, and it doesn't turn out as you thought, or it turns out horribly, and it changes your life in a way that you never thought was for the best. You have the power to choose how you view anything, so if you don't want to see the blessings and the benefits, then you are choosing to close the door to those opportunities.

A pity party is only for one. There will be no others invited, so you'd better choose wisely.

When we choose to live as if everything is exactly as it should be, we can adjust to the truth of the situation.

How many times have you said, If I had only known the truth, I could have dealt with it. **Truth will truly set you free,** and will give you healing, liberation, a deeper understanding, and appreciation for all that is given you in your life. I can remember situations when I wished for truth and understanding. But when I was given the truth, that allowed me to process, and then find a deeper understanding, and a more objective point of view.

Someone else's trauma is their journey, no matter how much you *love* them or want their *love*. It has never been about you!

We're all on our own journey to seek a higher and more compassionate understanding. If you want to find the treasure, it will be buried, and hard to find, but never as difficult as what you are doing now. You are a beautiful love and light that is connected to everything in the Universe, so think about it this way: You are on a planet at 98,000 miles per hour, and the fact that you are even standing up is a miracle! How is that even possible? How is it possible that we can see the stars that are millions of miles away? Get out of your head, and don't let that hurt inner child tell you what to do. Start to hear the cries of that hurt inner child inside of you, acknowledge and support them in a loving and healing way.

There are beautiful mind-blowing miracles everywhere, which evoke within us a powerful and moving emotional magic. These creations can move us to amazement and tears. Let yourself absorb these things every day. Love radiates outward, just as the sun's rays are felt from so many miles away. We are all connected to something so powerful and so infinite that we cannot avoid this beauty, radiance, and miracles every day.

About 96% of your body is made of the four most abundant elements of the universe. That means that you have only inherited 4% from your parents. Now, does it make sense to let that 4% control the other 96%?

Find a miracle every day, and you will soon see abundance; start with the small things each day, like nature, or water that comes out of your tap.... I'm still amazed that my phone can suck the Internet out of the air. How does it even do that???

Ask yourself, are we really the smartest creatures on the planet? I say NO, because we complicate our lives with lies, fear, guilt, shame, and abandonment. Does a whale care if it's fat? Does a baboon care if it's a baboon? What about an ass? Do they even know these derogatory labels that we've created? Do they even care? Maybe my childhood fantasy is true: We are some alien's 6th-grade bad science project, or we are the "Who's" from "Whoville" from Dr. Seuss's book *Horton Hears a Who*, living on a dust speck. Remember: "A person is a person, no matter how small."

So get out of your flawed head, and get into the miracles of everyday life. See how small and insignificant we are, and that we all have the same smallness on this infinite universal scale. No matter what our status, we all face the same problems and stresses, and we are all bound by the five emotions and the elements of the Universe. We all want to be *loved* and desired. But we often go on an endless search outside of ourselves for what is really already within us.

Remember when you're dealing with another human being: Sorry, it's never been about you.... It's always been about them........

When was the last time you took a deep breath?

Deep breathing is vitally important to your overall health, because it helps you oxygenate your cells and calms your nervous system. When you are in fight, flight, or freezing mode, your breathing gets very shallow, which means less oxygen goes to the brain, and your thinking is not so great. As you take a natural, deep belly breath every day, you will find a sense of calm and a release of urgency, which seems to fade away. Find moments in your day to belly-breathe just like you did as a baby, especially if you feel anxious, angry, or scared. Just breathe. Next time you are upset or see someone who is upset, tell them to take five deep breaths before speaking. Breathe, breathe, breathe, breathe, breathe.

CHAPTER 26:

The Eating Addiction and Solution

Diet Solution:

Have you ever gone to the store and seen a kid have an absolute meltdown at the candy aisle? Or when you have a second or third baby, and the older sibling starts to cry and is unhappy when they find out that you're pregnant? These are some common examples of the hurt inner child. We do the same as adults, and we can be very childlike when it comes to food choices. Fast foods, cakes, candies, chocolate, sodas, cookies, ice cream, pizza, chips, foods we can grab, or quickly prepared food choices that any seven-year-old can make. But when you're an adult, these behaviors could be related to unresolved childhood traumas; your inner child is looking for comfort foods to make them feel better. These comfort foods most likely were the same comfort foods as a child, or perhaps were shared with someone dear to you as a child. Foods are mood-altering drugs and have a significant impact on both the brain and the body. Most of the population lives in a mild chronic state of inflammation, leading to a host of medical issues such as anxiety, depression, fibromyalgia, IBS, Crohn's, gas, bloat, insomnia, diabetes, and cancer.

One of the essential amino acids that help process proteins is tryptophan. It enters the brain and the gut, and allows us to make more serotonin, our "happy drug." You can't make it on your own; the best way to get tryptophan is by eating a healthy nutritional diet. Tryptophan is found in whole grains, beans, and vegetables, which are the most nutritious sources and helps to reduce inflammation. Tryptophan is also a sedative, and whole grains will give you a calming and grounded feeling, making it easier to sleep. These are the healthiest foods to get tryptophan from, instead of eating dairy products that are going to cause an inflammatory reaction.

Serotonin is our happy drug, the ultimate mood stabilizer. We can't make enough of it without tryptophan. A diet deficient in tryptophan can lead to the following symptoms: depression, anxiety, aggression, mood disorders, poor cognition, suicidal thoughts, insomnia, and reduced motivation.

Low amounts of tryptophan will also lead to fructose malabsorption or fructose intolerance, which leads to IBS/Celiac disease, abdominal pain, bloating, diarrhea, or flatulence. Both fructose and sorbitol malabsorption will lead to a decrease of tryptophan, folic acid, and zinc in the blood, and it's important to note that about 90% of the serotonin levels are produced in the digestive tract.

Healthy gut bacteria are produced with whole grains, beans, and veggies, which helps serotonin production.

Alkalization:

One of the healthiest ways to stop growing cancer is to eat a plant-based diet, especially since many cancers are hormone-based, such as breast cancer. Whole grains such as brown rice, farro, steel-cut oatmeal, and barley is slightly acidic, and when chewed well, they become alkaline with the help of our saliva. Chewing is your most powerful and healthy food processor, and it's the best tool to grind up your foods. Not only does it help alkalize your foods, chewing starts your digestion and metabolism. You can chew and meditate 100, 200, 300 times during each bite until the food becomes liquid. As you slow down your eating, you'll start to sense the appreciation of what is on your plate.

All those beautiful colors in food are meant to heal your body and repair your organs. Find peace, happiness, and connection to a greater Universe, higher power, or God. Realize how powerful and unique you are from all other creatures and think about all that you have survived. You're exactly who you are supposed to be, and are connected to a higher power or source. Focus on becoming a compassionate human being; start to sense your connection to the earth and the Universe, something greater, something infinite that's outside of yourself. Remember that you are always connected. It's your gift, your right, and is infinite and everlasting.

Oxygenation:

Oxygen is vital for our survival, and one of the best ways to help increase our oxygen is to eat green leafy vegetables such as kale, collard greens, bok choy, or anything that contains chlorophyll. Oxygen, in turn, will help process our foods by oxidation, which turns our foods into liquid fuel. The more we chew our foods before swallowing, the more efficiently our bodies will process the food into fuel for energy, cell production, repair, and metabolism. This also reduces lactic acid build-up, which is responsible for pain in the body. In addition, as the oxygen fuels the cells, it allows them to repair any damage, thus helping them recover from diseases such as cancer. Another great activity to help increase oxygen levels is to take a walk in the woods. Since trees help produce oxygen due to chlorophyll in the leaves, the woods are a great place to practice your deep breathing.

Nitric oxide is also essential for relaxing blood vessels so that cells can receive more oxygen. To increase nitric oxide, breathing through your nose is one of the best ways because your nasal passage produces nitric oxide. Using some medical tape at night to help keep your mouth closed will increase restful sleep, reduce blood pressure, and lower inflammation. It's a weird sensation at first, but effective. You can also practice breathing through your nose throughout the day and during exercise.

One of the most important things you can do is: learn to BREATHE! We tend to hold our breath under stress, so take a nice, long inhale and then do a nice, long exhale. Some easy tricks are swimming, running, riding a bike, cardio exercises, diving, playing a wind instrument, speaking the word Om and drawing it out as long as you can. You can even play a game with yourself by using a pulse oximeter. On the meter, see how low you can get your pulse while getting your oxygen to 100.

What Happens in Vagus Goes Everywhere

You have another brain; it's in your gut. What you feed it will determine.......EVERYTHING! Imagine a huge telephone switchboard plugged into everything; and the woman running it is called, Vagus (nerve). She knows everyone and everything. She is the busy of the body. All your organs, heart, lungs, liver, kidneys, spleen....and yup, your brain too. Vagus is very sensitive so what you feed her determines how you're going to feel and react; the wrong foods can cause depression, anxiety, IBS, PTDS........ Vagus controls your moods, your immune responses and regulates digestion, so treat her with care.

Why don't you want to cook?

This is a frequent question I ask my patients. Many of them say, "I don't have time." So my next question is, "What is your favorite TV show?" If you have time to watch TV, you have time to cook, because no one inside that TV set is coming to save your life. They aren't going to pay your medical bills, and as a matter of fact, they don't even know you exist! So why are you spending so much of your quality time with them? Aren't you worth the effort? I know you are! Start simple with the foods you love, and make them healthier. Use a crockpot or rice cooker to save time; cook on the weekends. You are totally worth the investment. Spoil yourself with some spiffy new kitchen gadgets or spoons, knives, plates, and experiment with spices, beans, whole grains. Loving and nurturing yourself are your top life priorities, and that's not selfish. In fact, it's selfless, because the more you can give to yourself, the more you can give to others, leading by your healthy example.

Addiction and Foods

Every day we make choices about what we eat, and we rarely connect to what foods do to our bodies and how they affect our emotions. If someone asked you to eat a deadly mushroom, you wouldn't hesitate to say no, so what if the foods that you're choosing today, make you sick in the future and even shorten your life? What if they secretly sabotage your relationship with yourself, and others, and you sick, depressed, and lonely. Ask yourself some questions, "What emotion am I stuffing with my foods?" "Is this situation I'm going through now a reflection of a past situation?" "Maybe something from my childhood?" "I want mommy." "What is the benefit of my repeating it?" "Am I doing it because my inner child needs to please mommy or daddy so they will *love* me more?" "Do I feel that if I eat the foods that mommy or my *loving* guardian made, that is *love*?"

Start keeping a mood, food, and body journal: Here are some examples.

I binged on ice cream, and for the rest of the day, I felt bloated and depressed. I wish my mom were here to talk to me and make me feel safe.

I ate tuna (fighting fish), and later I argued with my kids. Then I ate chocolate to make myself feel better and went to bed depressed. I resent my kids because they have such a better childhood than I ever did.

Why couldn't my mom be that way with me, like I am with my kids?

My husband is so much like my father! Every time I talk to him, I get so frustrated, the only thing that makes me feel better is chocolate!

So how can we raise our serotonin levels with healthy foods that will help our mind, body, and spirit?

There are some awesome mood augmenters out there, and you can eat them every day! The first thing to remember is to eat every day; don't skip eating! Missing a meal will crash your blood sugars and make you feel depressed, even angry! Remember, serotonin is our new happy drug, the one we want to get high off, and the one solution our brain needs to de-stress.

These are some happy mood foods!

Dark green leafy greens, soybeans, edamame, tofu, tempeh. pineapple, butternut squash, seeds (sunflower seeds are a good one), black beans, tomatoes, mushrooms, broccoli, peas.

Whole grains: Amaranth, brown rice, corn, buckwheat, farro, barley, rye, wheat, kalmut, steel-cut oatmeal, quinoa, millet...etc. Whole grains are great mood stabilizers, especially when you cook them with sea salt or kombu seaweed. When cooking the grains, always add a pinch of sea salt or a postage stamp-size of kombu seaweed because they re-mineralize the brain, blood, and bone. Every day you incorporate these foods into your life will get you one step closer to a happier and healthier life.

There are some other foods that I want to tell you about that in Traditional Chinese Medicine are related to the five elements, five tastes, and all the body tissues. The body recognizes these foods as medicine, and they will help repair vital organs first, because they need these essential organs to survive. As a side-effect, the body will naturally lose weight and focus on repairing the organs first. These are excellent choices and some powerful medicines that can help you repair the cells in your body. **Remember, you get a brand-new body every seven years. How well it recycles will be your choice.**

Short-Grain Brown Rice: When chewed well, becomes alkaline and is hypoallergenic. It has the same protein-carbohydrate ratio as our bodies. When I was cooking for cancer patients, I used it daily. It's also loaded with vitamin B's, which helps calm the nervous system and relieve depression symptoms.

The following information can be found in three books:

The Self-Healing Cookbook, by Kristina Turner, *Helping Ourselves*, by Daverick Leggett, and *Healing with Whole Foods*, by Paul Pitchford.

Heart, small intestine, pericardium, san jiao: Fire Element: Loves bitter foods: Steel-cut oats, amaranth, rye, bitter greens, asparagus, artichokes, chicory, capers, watercress, scallions, rhubarb, pumpkin seeds, pistachio nuts, oregano, cinnamon, basil, cardamom, chamomile, chrysanthemum, coffee, dandelion root, tea.

Spleen, stomach, pancreas: Earth Element: Loves sweet foods: Carrots, corn, millet, sweet potatoes, butternut squash, acorn squash, spaghetti squash, sweet potato, pumpkin, brown rice, spelt, sorghum, wheat, flax, button mushroom, yams, water chestnuts, spinach, plantain, potatoes, most fruits, most beans, most seeds and nuts, kelp, ginseng.

Lung, large intestine: Metal Element: Loves pungent foods: Onions, garlic, wheat germ, broccoli, cabbage, caper, daikon, leek, mustard greens, parsnip, pepper, radish, scallion, turnip, watercress, bay leaf, caraway, chive, clove, ginger, marjoram, nutmeg, oregano, rosemary, sage, jasmine, peppermint, star anise.

Kidney, urinary bladder: Water Element: Loves salty foods: Barley, millet, nori seaweed, kelp, artichoke, olives, seaweeds, buckwheat, all beans (cook with sea salt or seaweed), all seeds and nuts, miso, tofu, tempeh, watermelon, sea salt, nettle, garlic, chive seeds, parsley, soy sauce.

Liver, gall bladder: Wood Element: Loves sour foods: Pickles, sauerkraut, wild rice, quinoa, rye, barley, lemons, limes, olives, apples, plums, apricot, blackberries, blueberries, cranberries, crabapples, grapefruit, lychee, oranges, pineapples, pomegranates, raspberries, tangerines, aduki beans, carob, hawthorn, purslane, tamarind, vinegar, rose hip.

CHAPTER 27

The Road to Happiness

Many of us think that pouring ourselves into someone will somehow make us feel *loved* and whole, but this is the total opposite of the road to happiness. Don't let those old "mirroring cells" let you mimic the "next best thing" to *love*. That's not how it works. We must first look in the mirror and interview the person in front of us. "Hello, my name is___________. It's really nice to meet you! I've heard a lot of awesome things about you, and I can't wait to know you better!" This is where you start every day and finish every day. You're it! You're the ONE! What you give to yourself, you will get from YOU! And what you get from you are the ingredients to your happy cake. What you bake inside yourself is what you eat every day, so bake yourself a happy cake with some loving and deliciously appreciative ingredients.

Charity: Not to others, but to *you*. How have you been charitable to yourself? Have you been listening? Spending time with yourself? How about taking the time to cook healthy? Getting out in nature, crafts, art, music, writing, self-healing.... etc. Have you been gentle to your body, mind, and spirit?

Faith: Know that there is something more out there than just you and other people. Take a look around you with fresh eyes and amazement, and question everything with a child's mind that is filled with excitement.

Hope: Admit it. You don't know everything, and you're not in charge, and the more you let go and trust, the more you will see a bigger picture. Trust that this wonderful and infinite Universe supports you, and all will be fine, for it's all part of our life's journey. There are lessons to be learned and healing to take place in order to have a deeper understanding of life and ourselves.

Love: Spread that on yourself like it's going out of style. No one, and I mean no one, is going to *love* you and fill your bucket as well as you will. Love truly is a magic power!

Gratitude: If you want the highest attitude, show gratitude. Be so mindful that you are chill with *every* situation. Have enough knowledge and insight to know that other people's stuff has nothing to do with you. It's their bucket, so no need for you to fill it or carry it.

When we fill our lives with these healthy ingredients: Charity, faith, hope, love and gratitude we will feel nourish in our body, mind and soul. These will help empower us in our daily life and enlighten our path.

Conclusion

Soul Journey

Life is a *soul* journey that no one can take for you; it's yours to take --wherever you feel you need to go, so go! You're not on this earth to rescue anyone. Just experience the incredible process of living the human experience. Everything is exactly as it should be, and when emotions come up, whether good or bad, simply journey within yourself to discover the answers. There's a rich vastness of wonders that lie within you. Magical and healing treasures that are there for you to discover, so that you can live a rich and whole life. The more disease exists in us, the further we have abandoned our own self-treasures. They are yours and yours alone, and when we seek treasure somewhere else, we have abandoned our own wealth. No one will help you or know what is deep within you. Only you can do that.

You are a beautiful gem, waiting to be discovered -- by you!

References:

https://www.mirecc.va.gov/docs/visn6/3_ptsd_checklist_and_scoring.pdf

1. Benedict, Marian "Pat." *The Silence of The Pain Is Deafening My Story*. Copyright 2016. Marian Marie Benedict
2. Bergman, Ingrid and Burgess Alan. *Ingrid Bergman: My Story*. London: Michael Joseph, 1980.
3. Black, Shirley Temple. *Child Star: Shirley Temple Black: An Autobiography*. New York: Warner Books 1988.
4. Blaustein, Michael. *The Human Brain Sees the World as an 11-Dimensional Multiverse*. New York Post: June 13, 2017.
5. Bradshaw, John. *Family Secrets: What You Don't Know Can Hurt You*. London: Piatkus 1995.
6. -----*Healing the Shame That Binds You*. Deerfield Beach: Health Communications, Inc. 1993.
7. -----*Home Coming*. London: Piatkus 2015.
8. -----*The Family: A Revolutionary Way of Self-Discovery*. Deerfield Beach: 1988.

9. Brinker, Nancy with Rogers, Joni. *Promise Me -- How a Sister's Love Launched the Global Movement to End Breast Cancer*. New York: Crown Archetype, 2010

10. Carroll, Diahann and Bob Morris. *The Legs Are the Last to Go, Aging, Acting, Marrying & Other Things I Learned the Hard Way*. New York: HarperCollins. 2008.

11. Chandler, Charlotte. *The Girl Who Walked Home Alone*. Simon & Schuster. New York. 2006.

12. Clark, David. *Broken Open*. Amazon Digital Services LLC. KDP Print US. Feb. 22, 2019.

13. *Criss, Peter and Sloman, Larry. Makeup* to Breakup: My Life in and Out of KISS. New York: Scribner 2012.

14. Dickinson, Janice. *No Lifeguard on Duty*. New York: HarperCollins. 2002.

15. Dobson, Christopher Editor-in-Chief. *Queen Elizabeth, the Queen Mother, Chronicle of a Remarkable Life 1900-2000*. New York, Dorling Kindersley 2000.

16. Etheridge, Melissa and Morton, Laura. *The Truth Is....My Life in Love and Music.* New York: Villard 2001.

17. Ewbank, Tim. Olivia: *The Biography of Olivia Newton-John*. London: Piatkus 2008 18. Ford, Betty and Chase, Chris. Betty, A Glad

Awakening. Garden City: Doubleday & Company, Inc. 1987.

19. Hamill, Dorothy and Amelon, Deborah. *A Skating Life: My Story*. New York: Hyperion, 2007.

20. Leggett, Daverick. *Helping Ourselves, A Guide to Traditional Chinese Food Energetics*. Totnes: Meridian Press 2003.

21. Locke, Sondra. *The Good, The Bad, & The Very Ugly a Hollywood Journey*. New York: William Morrow and Company Inc, 1997.

22. Mate, Gabor. *In the Realm of Hungry Ghost: Close Encounters with Addiction*. Berkeley: North Atlantic Books 2010.

23. Miller, Alice. *The Drama of the Gifted Child the Search for the True Self*. Basic Books 1979.

24. Pagles, Elaine. *The Gnostic Gospels*. New York: Vintage Books, 1989

25. Pease, Allan and Barbara. *Why Men Don't Listen and Women Can't Read Maps*. Broadway Books, 2000.

26. Perry, Simon and Petit, Stephanie. *Kate Middleton Admits She Was Very Naive as a Parent*, People Magazine. February 13, 2019.

27. Peters, Margot. *May Sarton: A Biography*. New York: Fawcett Columbine. 1997.

28. Pitchford, Paul: *Healing with Whole Foods, Asian Traditions and Modern Nutrition.* North Atlantic Books, 2002.

29. Rancic, Giuliana. *Going Off Script How I Survived a Crazy Childhood, Cancer, and Clooney's 32 on Screen Rejections.* New York. Three Rivers Press. 2015.

30. Redrick, Mia. *How to Deal with Mother's Guilt.* Huffington Post. 11/29/2011.

31. Reagan, Nancy and Novak, William. *My Turn: The Memoirs of Nancy Reagan.* New York: Random House 1989.

32. Dr Seuss. *Horton Hears a Who.* Random House, 1954.

33. Sikov, Ed. *Dark Victory -- the Life of Bette Davis.* Henry Holt and Company. New York: 2007.

34. Simon, Carly. *Boys In the Trees, A Memoir.* New York: Flatiron Books. 2015.

35. Soll, Joe. *Adoption Healing....A Path to Recovery.* Gateway Press, 2000.

36. Turner, Kristina. *The Self-Healing Cookbook.* Earthtones Press, 2002.

37. Unknown. *Blue Brain Team Discovers a Multi-Dimensional Universe in Brain Networks.* eurekalert.org, June 12, 2017.

38. Van Der Kolk MD, Bessel. *The Body Keeps Score Brain, Mind, and Body in The Healing of Trauma.* New York: Penguin Books, 2015.

39. Walfish, Fran. *The Self-Aware Parent.* St Martins Publishing Group. Dec. 7, 2010.

Online research topics: Veterinary studies in Bovines, Abandonment, Addiction, PTSD

My Story

I grew up in Avon, Connecticut in a house that backed up to a beautiful forest. I lived there with my mom, sister, and brother for the first 18 years of my life till I left home. I guess no childhood is easy, and mine was no exception, but we learn the "ropes" of survival to deal with the situations that come along.

My parents were in their mid 40's when I came along as proof that diaphragms don't work. At that time, there were three kids, my oldest brother David who is autistic, my brother Kevin and my sister Ginna. My sister was the princess with two older brothers and was six years old when I came along and disrupted her life. It was the first of March when my dad and my mom, who was eight months pregnant with me, decided it was best with the guidance of a doctor to place David into a state mental institute. He was 14 at the time. One month later, I was born just nine days before my sister's 6th birthday. Something she has never forgiven me for because my mom was going to take her to Howard Johnson's restaurant, but I changed all that. This was the beginning of the end for me and my sisters' *loving* relationship. With all the stress that my parents had and the guilt and shame of placing my brother Dave into the mental institution, needless to say, my six-year-old sister's world started to blow apart.

My father grew up in Iowa, where his family lost all their money and the bank they owned during the depression. My uncle Dave whom I never got to meet, bullied my father as a child. When my dad graduated high school, he followed his older brother to California to USC, where he met my mother.

My mom's family was wealthy because my great grandfather worked for Mass Mutual Life Insurance Company for 70 years. My grandfather went to Harvard and was an author and wrote screenplays for Charlie Chaplin. He was also a heavy drinker. My grandmother was a theater actress who traveled the country. At the age of 32, my grandmother became pregnant with my mother, whom she said: "ruined her career."

When I came along, the burdens of my parents' lives got the better of them. My father, who was passive-aggressive and a WWII vet, became an alcoholic and left my mother for another alcoholic, when I was two years old. My mother was diagnosed manic depressive and was in and out of the same mental institution as my brother. My father wanted to get divorced, but my mother would never grant him one. And four years later, my father killed himself in his girlfriends' garage.

I never knew what "normal" was, but I had my best friends who lived on the same road to spend time. They were the closest to normal I was ever going to get, and her parents took me in as just another one of the girls. What's one more when you already have five.

My mother struggled with her depression, but she was always a *loving* woman. And my sister took up where my dad left off with being passive-aggressive, and I was her primary target. So I had to leave home. There was no other choice because I thought about killing my sister. Not that I would, but the thought crossed my mind. I even told her to "kill me and get me out of her way" because that's how I felt. I was just in her way. She was the princess, and I was Cinderella; I needed to leave.

The Universe is a perfect place, and it sends you exactly what you need when you need it. Please be specific when you subconsciously ask, cause dam if the Universe fills in the blanks. When I was 17, I met my husband, and he was the first person who was nice to me. I had no clue about the interactions between males and females and how hormones when you're young are raging, telling you *love* lies, so you reproduce. No, I had no clue. So, at 17 and practically no dating experience after two weeks of dating, we decided we'd get married. He was moving to Florida permanently at the end of the month, and I had never even been south of Virginia before. Somehow, we'd be together.

So out of desperation to leave home, I found a college closest to where my husband and his family moved and applied. It's amazing what hormones will do to you when you're 18. Needless to say, I got in, and with that, he drove up from Florida to take me to college. Yes, insane, I know after only dating one month and not seeing him for a year......But we were in *love.* When everything is new, fresh, and exciting, everything seems wonderful, and then things start to etch and fade, little by little. We never really had any deep and meaningful discussions about life and responsibilities. We just lived like kids in *love,* living paycheck to paycheck and bouncing checks, and living off credit cards along the way. We were pretty much faking adulthood, unbeknownst to both of us, till one day I was pregnant. I was 19, unwed, had no insurance, no car, and was 1000 miles away from home. I still remember the smile on his face when I told him, and he said, without any hesitation, "You are? You know you can't keep the baby." And with that, I was going to have an abortion. There was never any discussion. I had never even been to the gynecologist before, so I had a friend from work take me.

It's bad enough going to the gynecologist, but the doctor who looked like Orville Redenbacher was pissed. He threw the card of another gynecologist at me and said, "here he can help you." After I told him I wanted an abortion. I never not wanted to be a mother. Being a mother was all I knew. It was all I ever saw. I never knew how to be a wife. This was just another trauma added to the pile of traumas I had experienced. I had always been fearful, and that fear has guided me into relationships involving death. I expected people to die and was sometimes disappointed when they didn't. My father's death has driven me to pick these people for relationships, and they have been dads. My drive to save them was the drive of a desperate child. I was trying to save my parents over and over again.

See, in the end, my manic-depressive mother and my severely depressed father, who committed suicide, taught me how to find a friend, partner, or *love* who was abusive and abandoned themselves and either dwelling on death or dying. And like the fantastic lifeguard that I am (because I spent my childhood trying to rescue my mother), I swam out into the deep waters to rescue them. The ironic thing about it is.... Newton's Third Law.... I never learned how to swim. No, really, I never did. I cried my way out of swimming lessons when I was a kid. Then when I was 25, I went to learn how to swim, and the swimming pool gave me a urinary tract infection to the point I went to the hospital. (Kidney, fear, essence of parents, death) And I almost drown myself trying to rescue others emotionally.

At first, I was blind to the patterns. You know, when your young, horny, and infatuated, everything seems wonderful, and I knew I could rescue anyone. My mother even wanted me to be a psychologist.... cause I was hers. Yes, I was going to *love* them and set them "straight," and like all good fairy tales, live happily ever after. So, I turned a blind eye to their seen and unseen trauma. But I could never walk or fit into their "shoes" or even begin to understand what they were going through, let alone myself. But like a beautiful rose that blooms, all these "flowers" (friends) had very large and unavoidable thorns. I'm an expert at picking these people who magically release themselves from me and their traumas by abandonment, alcoholism, cancer, suicide, and heart attack. There were even people who either threatened suicide or talked about dying and died. Even my own husband thought because his father died of the age of 35 of cancer, that he would die at that age too. (Thanks, dad. Even my child through abortion)

Yes, my wounds are deep, but they have made me an expert, and I am slowly drifting into the calmer waters of my life by taking a look at my own life, and looking at it like a dissected frog in 5th grade.

Bowels and all. Exposed. So now I meditate and cook the healthiest foods I can find. I never drank, smoked, or did drugs. I love to read, spend time in nature, exercise, and am constantly learning and growing into the person I want to become, and I am releasing all the unhealthy people and patterns that no longer serve me. It is much easier for me now to spot the patterns, and I have become more of an observer than someone who participates.

Life is truly a *soul* journey that no one else can take but you. It can take you to the "edges" of life, but you are always steering the ship. So be mindful and always navigate your "ship" into calmer waters, my friends.

One love

CPSIA information can be obtained
at www.ICGtesting.com
Printed in the USA
LVHW041456301021
701981LV00005B/19

9 780578 996509